PREY

The Secret That Almost Killed Me

by Brad Watson

ISBN: 978-0-578-76958-5

FOREWORD

Brad Watson has produced something unique. He has written a memoir that details the sexual abuse he suffered as a child and the lifelong impact of that abuse. But *Prey* is much more than a memoir. It is a challenge and it is a gift. The challenge: do you, the reader, have the courage to stay with him. The gift: if you do, you will understand what sexual abuse does to a child on a profound level.

The perspective of *Prey* is that of the boy going through the experience of grooming and abuse; his confusion, his fear, his inner and outer world being turned upside down. It is at first jarring to realize where you are, in his skin. It is a scary, bewildering place to be. And that is the point, and the gift of Brad Watson's memoir.

For survivors, it is necessary to issue a warning: prepare yourself, take precautions; best of all, read it with someone you trust so that you have a companion on this journey.

For those who love and care about survivors: Brad is truly offering you a gift, opening his wounded soul so that you can visit the time and the place – when and where the wound was created. But will you stay with him? Not the him who bravely re-enters his past to convey the reality of a child who endures sexual abuse, but the him who is the real protagonist here, the child. That is always our challenge, to stay with the child, to endure his fear and his suffering and not turn away from him.

Concretely, the challenge in reading Brad's memoir is not to skip ahead to the end of the book, the part where Brad the adult emerges, healed enough to write this riveting memoir. Yes, this story ends well. But the challenge to you, the reader, is to earn that ending, just as Brad himself has done.

Dr. David Lisak, founder of The Bristlecone
Project, Board of Directors – 1in6.org

AUTHOR'S NOTE

In writing this book I relied mostly on my own memory of events, as they occurred at this time in my life. When in doubt, I conducted research or contacted friends and family regarding the accuracy of certain facts. All characters and events in this book are real. However, I have changed the names and altered identifying details of most individuals to preserve their anonymity. My intent is to convey this part of my life with as much accuracy and detail as possible, while avoiding harm or embarrassment to those who may appear in the text.

For those still suffering in silence.

ONE

I couldn't see him, but I knew he was there. On my belly beneath the hedgerow, one move would give away my position. Dry crackly leaves surrounded me, and my left cheek was plastered with their spiky crumbs. Sweat rolled down my back and neck, and the air felt like warm bath water, as it often does in Central Texas in the summer. I was stuck, still not sure if he saw me, but knowing that if he had I'd probably be dead by now.

I could smell the weathered varnish from the cracking slat-board fence behind me, but mostly I smelled the ammonia burn of the chicken shit as it filled my nostrils from the coop on the other side. I knew the chickens were there but had forgotten about them until that moment. I was scared. Really scared. I'd never let myself get trapped back there before, and I wasn't sure what to do. My arms and legs started to shake a little, and I could hear the swishy cotton sound of my heart beating in my ears. It was keeping me from hearing other noises, and I still wasn't sure where he was.

I had to move. If I stayed there any longer, I was a dead duck. I'd seen it happen to others before, and I knew he wouldn't miss if I gave him a shot. He was ten years older than me, and his marksmanship was second-to-none, at least around our neighborhood. As I inched upward I could feel the leaves and twigs crunch under me more than I could hear them. A breeze finally began to blow through the leafy hedges, causing cool fingers of air to crawl up my stomach. My sweaty shirt stuck to me and made me shiver. I twitched my right arm forward a tiny bit, as good a time as any . . . .

BOOM!

I felt the sting of the shot and knew I was done. He hit me behind my right shoulder, just at the frayed edge of the cutout armhole on my Pittsburg Steelers t-shirt. The shot sent a ripple of pain all the way through my body. Though he'd hit me on the right side, the tingly shock went all the way through to my left arm. I dropped where I was, and this time I didn't notice the heat or the leaves or the sticks or the breeze or the smell created by thirty chickens living in a too-small coop in the heat of summer.

He got me.

I opened my eyes to darkness. Well, it wasn't entirely dark, but a lot darker than it had been outside. As my eyes adjusted, I saw the light of an aquarium in the corner, along with the fizz of bubbles coming up through a spongy looking rock in the corner of the tank. The puttering of the little air hose was the only sound. Six or eight small zebra-colored fish—the ones with pointy orange fins—darted through the water. He called them sharks.

I'd never been shot. I'd never been in his house or his room. I knew what happened when a real deer was shot, but what did one do with a seven-year-old boy-deer that'd been fatally shot with a Frisbee during a deer hunting game? Did he have a knife? Would he hang me up in the closet by my feet? My palms started to sweat.

So far, he'd followed the usual hunter's protocol—kill and drag the prey to an appropriate spot for cleaning.

With some hesitation, he started on my clothes. His voice was a little hoarse and he was visibly shaky as he explained what he was doing.

"We gotta get the shit and guts out," he said.

First my shirt, just like the deer's skin, so it would be easier to get at the stomach, heart, and lungs. He fumbled when he got to my pants. He unbuttoned the top, then stopped for a minute and seemed to catch his breath. He hesitated again, as if he didn't know what to do.

I was still supposed to be feigning death, so I clinched my eyes closed, but could hear him unzipping the plaid pants I wore most of second and third grade. He was pretty quick to get me skinned and seemed to be in a hurry to start the gutting. His hand was big. It felt like a catcher's mitt when he first touched me.

I jumped. His hand was on me. On my privates. No one had ever put their hand on me there. I clinched my eyes again because I didn't want him to know I had snuck a peek. I didn't know why, but for some reason I knew I shouldn't watch. He moved his mouth down. Electricity shot through my groin and down to my legs. I opened my eyes again to see what he was doing. It was the first time I'd ever felt anything like that. I'd only touched it when I needed to pee. The sensation shocked me. That wasn't part of hunter protocol.

The sad little filter pump tried to keep up with an aquarium that outsized it by at least three times. I laid there and thought about what had just happened—the hiding, the kill, the gutting, the honor of being in his room, the sound of his voice, the feeling of his super-wide hand, and the sandpaper rubbing sensation.

The fish darted up, down, left, right, chasing each other from one end of the aquarium to the other. A dingy slime covered the turquoise and blue rocks on the bottom, not enough to block out the colors, but just enough to indicate a day or two of missed cleanings. The fish swam low and a small cloud of crud floated up, mixed with the tiny bubbles, and made its way to the surface.

He got up quickly and went straight to the bathroom, calling over his shoulder with a little snip. "Better get your clothes on and get on home."

"Okay," I said.

What did I do wrong?

"Your mom will be wondering where you are," He'd lost the snip, but still sounded impatient.

"Promise you won't tell anyone about our hunting game?" he asked. "If anyone finds out, they'll want to play, and I'll have to change all the rules."

"Okay," I said.

"If grownups find out they'll be mad that we only play with each other and they'll make us play with everyone," his voice softened a bit more.

I didn't want him to have to go to all that trouble, and I surely didn't want anyone else getting any of my attention.

"I promise. I won't tell," I said, to no reply.

It got quiet. It was still mostly dark. I stood up and put my clothes on in a hurry – they were right where he'd put them after skinning me. Why had the game ended? I was confused. Walking through the short hallway I heard him peeing.

"I'm headed home," I said through the bathroom door.

Again, no reply. Nothing.

The heavy door closed behind me and I hesitated on the porch. My shoulders slumped as a light blanket of sadness settled over me. I felt like going back in. Something felt unsaid, but no words presented themselves. I turned and took a few steps, letting my heels slide off the curb, one by one. No reason to look both ways – I never did.

TWO

I crossed the street and headed toward my house, trying to figure out what'd just happened.

Why did he stop the game so fast?

Did I say something wrong?

Did I do something wrong?

My eyes were drawn to the yard across the street where we gathered to play football on the cold days after watching the real games on TV. It was edged with sticker burs and the fence-row was lined with pecan and hackberry trees. During and after the games, he always paid a little more attention to me, hugging me to the ground rather than tackling me.

Am I the only "special" one?

It felt awesome to be complimented by someone so much older than me, and better yet, by someone on a completely different coolness level than me, or any of my friends. I hoped I was the only one.

I looked down and noticed the purple and green burrs clinging to my shoelaces and white socks, and the start of a fresh scab on my knee from a skid on the gravel driveway the day before. Even though I'd followed Mom's advice and put hydrogen peroxide on it immediately, it still felt like there were a few bits of gritty rock buried down in there somewhere. There was the red streak of Monkey Blood I'd applied from the dark brown little glass bottle. I chose the Monkey Blood instead of the Merthiolate. If I was going to use Merthiolate, I might as well pour gasoline on my knee and call it good.

The narrow street, which didn't have a center stripe, and didn't need one, was lined with more pecan and a canopy of oak tree limbs. The whee uuur, whee uuur of cicadas buzzed in the air, and I plopped down on my front porch swing and daydreamed my way into the huge old American Elm in our front yard. It was a giant and shaded our whole yard and part of the street. Squirrels ran in and out of a small hollow about head high, and dead center of the trunk. I watched a drop of sticky, sappy juice run down from the hole, as the elm tried in vain to heal the void in its own heart. The hole was a bit smaller than a donut, but I imagined my way inside, enjoying a fantastic network of tunnels which connected hundreds of little rooms, each with tiny lamps and beds and chairs. I found myself there often. I loved the smell of the damp nutty wood from that old tree and the safe little room I'd concocted in the highest branch, reaching out over our house.

No one knew about the rooms. No one could find me there. I rocked back and forth on the swing, pushing against the loose porch railing with my right foot for momentum. Each push caused the square post to tip forward, ever so slightly. It made a muffled click as it settled back into place. The sound was hypnotic, and I lost track of time. Mom startled me with her call for supper. I'd rocked the whole afternoon away, and I felt better. After supper, we were going fishing.

Dad hooked up the trailer with the little flat-bottomed boat strapped to it. I ran my hand along the rim of the old faded green craft, as he clicked the hitch onto the back of his truck. The paint felt rough under my fingers, except where it had flaked off and exposed the smooth silver metal underneath. With a quick glance I made sure the line and sinker bucket was there and double-checked to make sure I hadn't left the bait box in the workshop. I felt responsible for the bait box because I was the oldest. It was there—the fat, tobacco-spitting yellow grasshoppers with those needley, grippy little feet stared at me through the rusty screen mesh container. The sides were made of screen wire and the top was just an old piece of inner-tube stretched across a small wooden frame with a slit down the center. I could get my hand in, grab a hopper, and pull it back out without losing even one of the others.

We'd caught most of the grasshoppers on late night spotlight hunts, on various winding, weed-covered roads on the outskirts of town during the few nights prior to this trip. They especially liked roadside ditches with thick stands of Giant Ragweed and Johnson grass. I'd shined my flashlight into the weeds and dove in, snatching wildly at the tiny glowing red eyes. I tried to grab them before they jumped. Sometimes I got a hopper, sometimes I got a handful of nothing.

"Make sure you get the hellgrammites," Dad said.

My stomach got flippy at the mere mention of them. They were harder to catch than grasshoppers, and much, much scarier. We'd caught the hellgrammites, or Eastern Dobsonfly larvae, on winter days or summer evenings when the river had been shallow, and the temps were at least tolerable. Slowly cruising the river, we'd found just the right island.

We'd waded in about knee deep and planted the poles that were attached to each end of our net. The chilly green current swirled past our legs, arching the net ever so slightly in the center. My brothers had walked around, upstream of the net and turned over any rocks and logs that looked like they could create a hiding place for our little prey. The escaping larvae, who'd been hiding under the slick mossy debris, floated right down into our waiting net. After catching the hard, multi-sectioned, pinchy little bugs, we'd taken them home and dumped them into big zip lock bags and saved them for a day like this.

I ran back in to the house, grabbed one of the largest bags out of the freezer, and put it next to the grasshopper bait box. Hopefully they would thaw by the time we started setting our lines. They were dead – frozen in time by the hard block of ice in which they were incased. But hellgrammites were still scary, even though some of them had been frozen since last year. I glanced down at my bare feet. The band-aid on my middle toe looked like it was about to come off. I'd sliced the skinny toe on a piece of jagged scrap-metal in Dad's workshop the day before. It still hurt. But I knew what would hurt worse. The cut throbbed a little at the thought of hellgrammite pincers on my toes, or worse, the skin between.

What if they're like goldfish and can come back to life after being frozen?

They stank. But the channel cats liked them. I spontaneously opened the bag. The whiff of earthy, dead cricket smell made my heart skip a beat. I knew we'd be pulling in a 10-pounder later.

The wheels squished through the gooey mud that was plastered over the broken concrete boat ramp. We pulled in and prepared to launch our boat. I bailed out of the passenger side of the truck while my brothers bailed out of the back. They argued about who had spilled the Coke on the seat as the tree frogs merrily sang their chorus. Dad backed the boat into the water until the trailer was completely submerged. The red boat-trailer lights were fitted with special gaskets, so they didn't short out or crack when they were submerged. The rosy glow of those little bulbs slowly disappeared as they slipped silently beneath the dark water. I hung on to the rope as the boat slipped off the trailer and out into the racing water. The slack caught and lurched me forward as the nose tried to head downstream. I leaned back and dug my toes into the cool mud for the little extra traction I could get.

I gripped harder at the mushy river bank with my toes and pulled the nose of the boat back around in our direction. I just barely got it out of the water and onto the small shelf below the upper bank.

Whew.

For a moment, the wet, yellow nylon rope had almost slipped out of my hand. I thought the current was going to get the best of me and take my Dad and his boat down the river before he was ready. After pulling it up on the little rocky shelf and double checking to make sure it was secure, I paced a small rut into the mud as I waited for him to crank the motor. Sometimes the 25-horse Johnson outboard started, and sometimes it didn't. It was never a sure thing. I knew that if it didn't crank, Dad would figure it out and fix it – he could fix anything.

"Goddammed no good mother fucker," he said, as if the motor was a person. He pulled on the frayed little starter rope again. "Piece of shit motor. No good, goddammed choke," He pulled. He yanked. "Well, this just chaps my ass."

He pulled again. I was sure the rope would break. Blue-grey smoke swirled and then settled on the surface behind him as the little Johnson rumbled, gurgled, and then went silent again. He yanked the cover off and turned some screws. Not quite sure if we would be going fishing or not, my little path in the mud got deeper as I paced my worry.

One more pull. Two more. Sputter. Knock. Sputter knock sputter. And…she cranked. As I watched the insides of the motor begin to spin faster, it clattered and rattled in defiance. Finally. Dad swung the beat-up white cover up in an arc and plopped it down in its place with one swift motion. Clack. Clack. Both clamps were in place.

Both of my brothers hopped in while the boat was still secure. I gave it a push and simultaneously swung my muddy feet over the lip and onto the flat aluminum bench in front. We slid away from the small shelf and out into deeper water. Dad turned the boat upstream and twisted the black rubber throttle all the way around. He gave it everything. After a few initial sputters, she opened up and the sputters turned into a smooth buzzing hum. Yes…we were going fishing today.

We took flight down river. I was in heaven. It was late evening, the sun was low in the sky, and the organic, vegetative smells of the river filled my nose. The cicadas and tree frogs came alive and could be heard over the sound of the motor. Wind blew the hair that was sticking out from under my backwards facing ball-cap back out of my face and the sticky humidity from my bare forehead. The river was winding, with piles of drift stacked against fallen trees in every bend. Fallen logs and limbs bobbed up and down, struggling against the current, as it hurried the water off toward the Gulf of Mexico. The current was strong. Mom's voice echoed in the back of my mind, "If you get pulled under, you'll die". The river was beautifully dangerous. I felt alive, really alive.

My brain was on fire. I knew we were staying up really, really late. The oncoming darkness only added to the energy of the river and made it seem more fun, and scary. We'd just begun baiting our lines. I knew we would "run" them until Dad got tired and said we were done, or until the fish shut down and stopped biting, whichever came first. My eyes scanned the bank for life. I usually spotted a raccoon, possum, deer, nutria, or maybe even a snake near the edge of the water. It became a blur as we sped downstream.

I glanced down and noticed the spools of line in the bottom of the boat. Some were wrapped around sticks. Others were spooled around Coke cans or bottles. Each of our "trotlines" and "drop lines" consisted of heavy braided green nylon fishing line with a series of hooks attached by their own one-foot leaders, six to ten feet apart. As I looked at the spools, with shiny hooks sprawled in every direction, I wondered how any of them could possibly be unwound without getting tangled.

Dad knew just where to deploy the lines and which kind to use. The first was in a shallow, slow-moving eddy, so we put out a trotline. Dad expertly moved the boat into position, between a floating mass of limbs, sticks and vines, and the nearest bank. My brothers both grabbed at a tree-limb hanging out over the water. After grabbing a limb, and having Josh, my youngest brother, hold on for dear life, Luke, the older of my two younger brothers tied one end of the slippery green line on.

"Let go." Dad yelled at Josh over the noise of the engine and idled the motor as we drifted downstream to the other tie-off limb.

Luke attached the hooks with a cool loop-knot as we made our way down the line, making them easier to remove when we had fish on later. He tied one on and we slipped downstream a few feet. He tied another and we continued down until they were all on.

As my brother was tying off all those hooks, with those cool loopy knots, I sat by and watched. Although he was doing the risky work with the hooks, a subtle fear crept up through my torso. Why was I scared? I'd done this a hundred times. I imagined myself getting sucked under the brown, boiling water and struggling to come back up. My pulse quickened as I thought about the slippery, giant, yellow grey catfish that I knew was down there – the same one we were trying to catch. I pictured it grabbing my legs with its wide, whiskered mouth and sandpaper teeth, and holding me under until my lungs exploded. My stomach seemed to fill with heavy cement, and I felt it moving down through my intestines.

Maybe I was just a wus. My brothers didn't seem scared. They were younger than me. I couldn't shake it. I thought about the fat, blue-green mother alligator gar with her scales the size of arrowheads, living under the adjacent sunken tree. I shook a little as I imagined her eating me chunk by chunk with her long blunt snout, lined with hundreds of pointy needle-sharp teeth, and leaving nothing for my parents to find. Then I saw myself getting a 6/0 hook stuck in my hand while I was shoving it through that juicy yellow grasshopper and getting yanked out of the boat and held under by that window weight just below the surface, and just out of sight. Panic surged through me. I'd be stuck there. I'd have no choice but to breathe in that warm sandy water.

I loved being on the river. I hated that it scared me. I felt weak. I wanted to ask Dad if he thought any of those things would really happen…just to hear him say that they wouldn't. But I didn't mention it.

The water didn't scare me. Neither did the catfish, the gar, or the hooks. Drowning and dying didn't even scare me. But I almost couldn't bear the thought of Mom and Dad looking into the water and wondering where I was and what had happened to me. I felt their fear. I felt their sadness. Tears started to warm my eyes. I made sure no one saw. What was wrong with me anyway? I looked toward the opposite bank until my eyes stopped burning.

I snapped out of it. We were fishing. Dad was in charge of the boat and I was busy baiting hooks. A slight breeze caused my shirt to flap gently against my back. The corner of my mouth turned up slightly – almost a smile – as the muddy organic odor found my nose again. I looked over my shoulder at Dad. He sat on his little square boat cushion, watching his boys doing what he'd taught them. He was in charge. The warmness washed over me so suddenly I almost teared up again. I was safe.

THREE

I glanced over my shoulder at the table near the porch. Red, yellow, green, blue and white presents were jumbled together. Someone had knocked them over and they were scattered everywhere. Some were on the table, some on the ground. I looked hard but couldn't find the one I hoped would be obvious.

Flies buzzed around the blue cake and one of my aunts was charged with swatting at the annoying little buggers with a colorful Happy Birthday paper plate. The icing was the hard sugary kind. Large, finger-thick cracks had started making their way around the sides, as the temperature rose, and the cake dried out. I liked the soft creamy icing better, but that didn't matter. This was an extra special kind of birthday because Dad had the homemade ice cream maker sitting up on the porch, and Mom had chopped the baseball-size Fredericksburg peaches the night before. The ice was there. The salt was there. The other sweet and creamy ingredients were there – sugar, cream, and most important for me, vanilla extract.

I loved vanilla extract. I wanted it so bad, I could already taste it. The creamy, sweat smell drove me crazy and I just couldn't wait for Mom to open the little black screw top. She opened it up, and out came that aroma. I sniffed it. I licked it off of each utensil that had touched it. I licked some off the table. I even used my finger and wiped up a little bit off of the floor.

I went just a little bit crazy when I saw Mom stop using the spoon and dump more than was needed into the peach ice cream mixture. I wasn't sure how much was called for, but it seemed like she used a lot. Once all the ingredients were in, I watched the little cylinder spin. The ice rattled as the motor whined and kept its rhythmic pace. Mom asked me to add more salt to the ice. I did. After a few more turns the whine got louder and the spin got slower. The time was getting near. It was almost ready.

The gritty texture and pure taste of that homemade ice cream was better than the second rate, creamy, store bought ice creams sitting on the table and softening up for those who'd want seconds, or those who'd showed up late. We only got one serving of the good stuff. But it was so good. Good enough to last until the next time our whiny spinning little alien was brought out of its box and asked to do its dance. It's sweet, creamy, too much vanilla dance.

We all ran around the yard yelling and playing "tag" and "it". I could feel the Coke and candy-induced energy pushing me along as my cousin, who was "it", tried to catch me. Next, we all gathered around and pinned the tail on the poor donkey that had already managed to get himself pinned up on our carport wall. Everyone played, even the older kids. Someone spun me around in circles and pushed me forward. My head swam, and I felt my stomach flip a little. I had no idea which way I was walking. I bumped into a hard surface, which I assumed was the wall. As I pushed the pin into the wall, everyone laughed. My cheeks automatically flushed. I missed the whole donkey. Eventually my cousin stuck him right in the sweet spot and received a little gift bag filled with candy and plastic rings. I acted as though I didn't care. Plastic rings were stupid and only for little kids.

The piñata was huge. A hulking blue bull with curved white horns, fiery red eyes, and an extra layer of thick, fringy piñata fur. His nose was cone-shaped, kind of like a beak, but the rest of him looked like a bull. I wondered what could possibly be inside his cardboard hide. I knew we'd soon find out.

The smaller kids took their turns. They swung and missed a bunch. Finally, the bat was shuffled my way. The birthday boy was about to have his turn. I gripped the sandpaper tape on the bat handle. The rough grit felt good in my hands.

I could just barely see through the red bandana that was tied around my head. Light came through first, and after a second or two, shapes started appearing. It was supposed to keep me from seeing the giant of a bull that I'd be swinging at, but I could see him as clear as anything. I didn't mention it.

I swung half-heartedly the first time. "Strike one," my brothers and cousins yelled simultaneously. I smirked behind the thin blindfold. I acted confused, as if I wasn't sure which way to swing. They laughed. I shuffled my feet in a half circle and put all my leverage into one violent swing. CRACK. I watched the rear half of the big blue bull tear away. In the same instant, an avalanche of candy rained down onto the carport floor.

The rattley sound of hard candies hitting the concrete seemed to last for a full minute. The sheer amount of bounty that was stuffed into that single piñata made my jaw drop and I hesitated just enough for the others to get the jump on me. My feet were frozen in place. They pounced on the colorful candy carpet and started filling their party piñata bags full of the wonderful treats I'd unleashed.

Suddenly, I snapped out of it and ripped the see-through blindfold off. I jumped to the middle of the pile and began shoving smaller kids out of the way. Soon, my bag was stuffed with as much candy as would fit and I quickly realized it wasn't going to be big enough. After crumpling the top of the sack down and stashing it under the table, I began shoveling candy into the folded-up tail of my t-shirt.

The melee was done. I sat down and surveyed the goods – Charleston Chews, Bazooka Gum, Necco Wafers, Slo Pokes, Hot Dog Gum, Saf T Pops, Flipsticks, Lick O Sticks, Razzles, Satellite Wafers, Bit-O-Honeys, Atomic Fireballs, Caramel Creams, Tootsie Rolls, Dad's Rootbeer Barrels, Candy Buttons, Smarties, Candy Cigarettes, Nestle Crunch, Dots, Gobstoppers, Now and Laters (strawberry was my favorite), Pixy Sticks, Fun Dip, Pop Rocks, Chick-O-Sticks, Fizzies, Dubble Bubble Gumballs, Boston Baked Beans, Bonomo Turkish Taffys, Snickers, Milky Ways, and 3 Musketeers. It had all been in there, and it was all wonderful.

My teeth hurt from chewing candy. I could already feel a burning ulcer forming on the left side of my tongue from all the sugar I'd just eaten. I was rubbing my tongue on the inside of my teeth and just thinking about complaining when Mom spoke up.

"Anyone wanna open presents?" she asked.

That's what I'd wanted all day. My mind raced. There were so many. Was it there? I'd been looking. I hadn't seen it. My heart skipped when I looked over at the extra-long picnic table. Someone had re-stacked all the gifts, but there were still too many to fit on top. Some were leaned on the sides and some were stacked on the ground underneath. Everyone scurried over and gathered around. I surveyed the jumble as I walked over. Trying not to be too obvious, I still wasn't finding what I was looking for. I stopped and waited for Mom to give me the word. All eyes were on me as everyone hoped I'd pick their present first.

As I dug into the pile, I was only looking for one box. Only one. One shape. One size. One present. I pushed aside the small square packages and flung the lighter flat ones out of the way...they obviously contained clothes. It wasn't there. I couldn't find it. Surely there was some mistake? I hadn't asked for anything else.

Everything suddenly seemed to be happening in slow motion. I just stood there for what seemed like a minute or two. After the initial flurry of activity had failed to produce the results I wanted, I reassessed my strategy. This time, I sorted through the avalanche of gifts one by one, hunting for clues as to the contents of each one as I went along.

And then...there it was. The end of a box, with an unmistakable shape. I'd been in such a hurry I'd tossed it aside with some random boxes of guaranteed clothes. It lay mostly covered up, about mid-pile. Just the one end was visible, but I knew it was the one.

Again, I tried not to be too obvious. I'd been trying since the party began, and the whole week before. I'd methodically searched Mom and Dad's closets and the attic and tried to cover my tracks as best I could. Now I felt such a pressure in my body, like I might explode. The buildup had been unbearable.

The package was half as tall as me and at least as wide. The blue and green wrapping paper was re-taped over a small rip on one of the corners. I was even more excited, because I knew what had caused that rip. I slowly removed the tape, trying not to rip the already ripped paper. As I pulled apart the long seam going up the entire length of the back of the box, I finally saw it. It was only the image on the back of the box, but the excitement peaked, and I violently ripped the rest of the paper off and flipped the box over to reveal what I'd really been waiting for. It was now staring me in the face.

The flaming orange, rubbery plastic tracks of my very own Hot Wheels Drag Race Action Set! It was all there, the tracks, the flat clear tabs to connect them, and the spring-loaded starter that attached to the end and sent the cars burning down the strip at top speed. I shredded the box getting the pieces out and set it up right there on the driveway. It only took a few seconds and we had our own speedway ready to go.

I raced them all…the orange Corvette, the blue Mustang, the square red ambulance with stickers for lights, the green dune buggy, the white tow-truck with the plastic boom and cable, and my all-time favorite, the black super van with reddish orange flames and little plastic chrome mufflers running down each side. I raced it over and over. It looked so real. I saw myself inside the little black window, sitting in the driver's seat, punching the gas and grinding the gears. My mirrored sunglasses reflected the losers as I looked back at them and sped away.

After the racing was done, I opened the other presents and set them aside, not paying much attention to them. The van was my favorite. A little bit heavier than the others, it won every time.

It was time for the party to end. Mom was thanking everyone for coming and some folks were already driving away. I looked down at the van…my van. I placed it in the very top of my Hot Wheels 24-car Super Rally Case. It had earned its spot as the leader of the pack. I imagined the van looking down on the other cars and trucks for their poor performances on the track, and for their lack of badass flames.

FOUR

I topped the riverbank and thought about going in the back door to tell Mom I was headed down to Grandma's house. I didn't. I pointed myself toward the two-track road that lead from the back of our acre-and-a-half and up to the paved street. My bare feet shuffled through the loose gravel and up the hill. I was ready to get there. If I'd gone in to tell Mom, there may have been some chore to do first. Grandma's house was fun. No chores. No scolding. She would even pay me money to eat bowls of cereal. If I finished one bowl, I could make a quarter. I would have finished it anyway. But at Grandma's I got a quarter. My record was a dollar.

Like all the houses on the street, ours sat nearly one-hundred yards from the upper river bank. The property sloped upward from the water and ended near a line of pecan trees along the street in front of our house. As I walked up the path, I noticed a few old Hot Wheels half-buried in our sand pile. The black van with the cool flames was a little scratched up and hadn't seen its special place in the Hot Wheels 24-car Super Rally Case since I bent one of the back wheels by accidentally running over it with my bike a few weeks earlier. Cars and trucks that had been inflicted with career-ending injuries such as this were typically moved down to the B-Team and ended up in the sand pile, which was just like a sandbox, only it was a pile, and wasn't in a box. My chest still tightened every time I saw it there in the sand. It had won so many races.

"Hi," I called to the neighbor across the overgrown fencerow, which was thick with yellow and orange honeysuckle. He didn't look up from his weed trimming.

The fencerow ran from the street all the way down to the river. I stopped and plucked a couple of the trumpet-shaped blooms from their vine. I surgically removed the tiny little bump on the small end of the first flower and pulled the delicate little stem down through the tube. The dewy golden drop wasn't much, but it was worth the effort. Though it was itty bitty, it was super sweet. It was also super cool to drink the same liquor that hummingbirds drank. I plucked five or six more and continued on to Grandma's house, which was only three houses down from ours.

I knew every blade of grass, every exposed pecan tree root, and every gopher hole along the way. I walked to Grandma's almost every day and this seemed like just another day. The air was warm and heavy, and billowy gray clouds kept the temperature down to a tolerable level and looked like they could drop their tremendous loads at any time. Cicadas were starting their evening serenade, and I was planning to spend the night at my Grandma's house, although I hadn't told her yet. It was also my Paw Paw's house, but we never called it that.

Somewhere along the way I heard the call.

"Hey. How about some football?"

I looked all around to see where the voice was coming from. I expected to see him in the yard with a football, but instead, he was standing in his front doorway waving me over. Maybe we'd have something to drink before the game. I walked in and he was pointing toward the TV. I finally got it. We were going to watch some football, not play some football. That was okay with me, because I loved watching it almost as much as playing it. My chest swelled a little. I tried not to show my excitement. He could watch the game with anyone…but he'd chosen me.

He was eating something, and tiny white crumbs were caught in the wrinkles of his NFL football shirt. It had striped half sleeves, a number on the front and a famous name on the back. His cutoffs were too short, and the zipper was half unzipped. He didn't have on underwear and I could see his pinkish tan skin where his underwear should have been.

"Sit down." He pointed to the spot next to him on the couch, and we watched the two teams battle back and forth trying to improve their pre-season records.

I was startled when his hand touched me.

We weren't playing the deer hunting game, and he'd never touched me without games—football, or wrestling, or the hunt.

His hand was half on my crotch and half on my exposed leg, which looked chicken-skinny coming out of the bottom of my frayed cutoffs. He commented on a bad call by the ref, as my heart raced, and I heard that swishy sound building in my ears again. I was completely caught off guard. I panicked and jumped off the couch. It was broad daylight, and anyone could just walk in and see us. My face flushed. My ears got hot and I thought they might even be moving as they throbbed. I suddenly felt guilty…and afraid of being seen or found out, though I didn't know why.

I sat back down on the noisy couch, after some coaxing, and got back into the football game. A bit later, his hand was back on my crotch.

"No one's coming home soon," he said. "The windows are half-shaded anyway."

I had no argument, so he left his hand there for a while, and then he put it inside my pants. It didn't seem right to watch him, so I turned my attention to the deer, which was mounted and stuck up on the wall in the corner, facing the door. He appeared to assess anyone coming through the front door. He was magnificent. His orangey brown horns were heavy and tall with little stickers protruding from the base, up to about the third point. His tines were thick and long, curving inwards to form a perfect basket rack. His head was angled, and he looked down on us as we did what we did, his dead glass eyes not giving away his thoughts.

After a few minutes, he used my hand to help him finish his business. I didn't look down. It still didn't seem right to look. He got up, grabbed some tissues from the end table and made a quick trip to the bathroom. He came back quickly and ate a couple of cookies from the counter. We talked about the football game until it was over.

I walked to Grandma's house and had a bowl of Frosted Flakes. She gave me a quarter.

FIVE

A single drop of sweat dripped down my spine. The back of my shirt was already wet, in the outline of the chair-back of my wooden desk. Everyone in class was frowning and some of the girls had made fans out of notebook paper. The girl next to me had decorated her fan with bright neon drawings of orange and red ladybugs. She was not willing to share the wind she created.

A blue norther had come down out of Canada the week before. It was gone now. Ms. Robinson opened the creaky side-hinged casement windows in hopes of catching what little early September breeze there might be outside. The window unit in our classroom was on the fritz and the hope of that slight breeze was on all our minds. We were on the northwest side of the top floor of that little tan brick schoolhouse. The school was a perfect rectangle, and when the south wind was blowing, which it did throughout the summer and into those first few weeks of school, we got nothing. No breeze. No wind. No saving coolness.

I sat in the third row, wiping sweat from my face with the tail of my un-tucked shirt and tried to learn the new multiplication and long division problems that Ms. Robinson had assigned a few minutes before. I'd been carrying my 4 by 6-inch flashcards with me every day of third grade and gave the ones I'd already learned to my buddy, Woody.

Woody had been my best friend since we got into trouble over some Hot Wheels transactions we'd conducted way back in Ms. Frank's first grade class. Trouble had a way of finding Woody.

As I looked over at him wiping sweat off his face too, I thought back to that day in first grade. I'd seen him get into trouble before, but it was a first for me. I'd brought a check to school for the first grade book fair. The thought of the new ink and the still-warm paper smell of all those books made me giddy. I had my mind set on ordering the Berenstain Bears: The Bears' Vacation, The Big Honey Hunt, Bears on Wheels. I would only be able to afford one or two, so I'd have to choose wisely. I liked the bears so much in first grade that I imagined being a bear and living in their big tree house. I imagined a safe room on the top floor, just like my little room in the giant elm in our front yard.

So, I'd brought the book money to school that morning, and Woody had brought some cool Hot Wheels. Somehow, Woody had talked me into giving him my book money check. In return, he'd given me a shiny new Hot Wheel. It was a straightforward transaction. Woody and I had both been happy. Then, the time to order our books came. I'd taken the order form, looked down the extensive list of titles, and picked out the two that I knew would be my favorites – both Berenstain Bears. I'd checked the boxes. I'd signed my name. I was supposed to include check or cash, but I didn't have check or cash. Woody had taken my check or cash and I had a classic red 36 Ford Coupe. It was one of the coolest Hot Wheels I'd ever seen. But I couldn't buy my books with a Hot Wheels classic red 36 Ford Coupe.

I'd cried, and my teacher took me out into the hall. She didn't leave me much choice, so I told her about the check and the Hot Wheels and the Berenstain Bears and how mad Mom was going to be when I told her. She called Mom. Woody got licks. Mom sent another check the next day and I ordered my Berenstain Bears titles.

The girl next to me dropped her fan and I snapped back to multiplication problems. Fourteen multiplied by fourteen?

Woody sat next to me on that sweltering September day. He sat in a broken desk to my left. We'd gotten in trouble a couple of times for talking. And he was getting in trouble again, not for talking, but for rattling his broken desk on purpose. Instead of fixing or replacing the desk, Ms. Robinson just yelled at Woody every time it rattled.

He had told me the day before to bring a new pencil and three of those large round erasers that fit on top. I had no idea why I needed to bring these ordinary supplies or why he sounded so excited about them. I had extra school supplies at home, and I showed up with a fat green No. 2 pencil and three unused erasers – one pink and two blue.

"We're going to erase the skin off the top of our hands," Woody said excitedly.

That sounded great. It was a contest to see who could erase skin the longest without stopping.

I could tell by the quick, jittery way he was talking that he'd planned this for a long time. Woody usually talked slow and low, with a slight Hispanic accent. He kind of over-pronunciated his words and it made everything he said sound very important.

"We'll get started as soon as Ms. Robinson gives us our assignment and leaves the room," he whispered.

It sounded like an easy contest and I was sure I would win. All I had to do was rub the eraser on top of my hand longer than Woody.

Ms. Robinson handed out our multiplication assignment and left the room. I looked at the packet of papers.

"Should we wait until lunch?" I asked. "It'll be hard to finish fifty problems and have enough time to rub erasers on top of our hands."

"You chicken?" Woody asked me.

I assured him I was not.

So, we erased. I chose the pink eraser first and began rubbing it on the back of my left hand, between my index and middle fingers. It was easy to keep it on track because of the raised tendons under the skin. I moved the eraser back and forth and it stayed in the natural groove.

"Is this fast enough?" I asked without really knowing why.

"I guess," he answered.

It didn't take long for the burning to start. All the fuzzy little hairs were gone. I saw the skin turning pink, but I thought it was just because I'd started with the pink eraser. As I rubbed and rubbed, the burning got worse and worse. My eraser started getting wet, and Woody suddenly stopped and put his head down on his desk. I thought he was mad because I rubbed my eraser longer than he rubbed his, but his thick, black frizzy hair was bobbing up and down and I knew he was crying. He wouldn't raise his head or show me his hand. Ms. Robinson walked back in as I was trying to pull his hand out from under his desk.

"Stop roughhousing and finish your multiplication packets."

My hand was on fire, but I didn't let it show. It felt like I'd rubbed it with hot charcoal instead of a cold pink eraser. Pinkish clear liquid oozed out of the two-inch long groove I'd erased into my hand. I hoped Ms. Robinson's nose wasn't sensitive enough to pick up the faint smell of burning rubber. I hid it and tried to finish my packet while Woody cried louder and asked if he could go to the nurse. He said he had a stomachache. The right side of my mouth turned up, just a little.

I win.

I worked on my packet for ten or fifteen more minutes and there was a knock on the classroom door. A student from the first floor, probably a second grader, brought a note in and handed it to Ms. Robinson. She read the note and her head immediately spun around in my direction. We locked eyes before I could look down.

Woody!

He'd ratted me out.

Ms. Robinson asked me to follow her to the nurse's office and I was forced to show them my leaky hand. By then it was an inflamed, oozy, bloody mess. I still didn't cry. The clear pinkish liquid had started down my fingers and was dripping on the floor.

"How did your hand come to be in this condition?" the nurse asked.

"I rubbed it with a pink eraser on a green number two pencil," I replied, not quite able to meet her eyes.

She laughed so loud I was sure my classmates on the third floor could hear.

"And why would you do something like that?" she asked, still laughing.

I didn't have an answer. There was no answer. Woody had asked. I had accepted.

The nurse confessed that when he was alone with her, before I'd been brought down, Woody had confessed that the whole eraser-rubbing contest had been my idea. I had hatched the entire scheme. I had been the one who asked him to bring the pencil and erasers to school. I had been the one to encourage him to start the rubbing that morning, and when he hesitated, of course I had asked if he was a chicken. He'd told me he was not.

It was all my fault and without my bad influence, Woody wouldn't be sitting in the nurse's office with a deep, second degree friction burn on the back of his damn hand. Of course, my story differed from Woody's…slightly. When neither of us would change our version of events, the nurse decided we needed to pay a visit to Principal Day.

I'd managed to find myself in his office a couple of times during my three years at Central School, but those had been minor infractions and usually ended with a stern talking to and a note home to my parents. This was a little different due to the fact that Woody and I were both injured and neither of us would change our version of the truth. It was my word against his. One or both of us was lying.

I looked up at Mr. Day. His thick arms were folded across his midsection. He leaned back slightly in his chair and looked up at the water stained ceiling tiles, as if trying to figure out what he should do with us. After what seemed like an hour, he decided the best course of action for a couple of third graders who had burned a hole in their hands with erasers, one of which was obviously lying, was for both of us to get licks.

"Do either one of you want to change your story?" Mr. Day asked. He looked at Woody first.

"Nope," Woody said defiantly. He didn't look up.

"Nope," I said, looking at Mr. Day and jerking my eyes to the left, as if to tell him Woody was the one lying.

My telling glances didn't work. He made Woody leave the room. He moved his name plaque, a little rubber statue of a man holding a football, and a couple of stacks of paper held together with big old scissor-style clips. I placed my bandaged left hand and my good right hand on his desk. Pink oozed through the thin little gauze bandage the nurse had tried to apply while laughing at me. The corner of my mouth turned up slightly, again. I'd won the contest. Woody had quit. And, he'd cried. I'd won.

Mr. Day looked me in the eye and asked, "Do you know why you're getting licks?"

"Yes, but Woody's lying," I explained.

"Since no one saw you two fools rubbing your hands, I can't choose which one of you to believe," he responded.

I knew what was coming. I could see every grain of wood on that baseball bat sized instrument of pain. It looked huge and I saw splinters coming out of the side he was about to hit me with. His arms were bulging with veins and muscles. I had never been paddled in school and I was already crying. Fear and embarrassment fought for control of my mind. I felt bees in my stomach and almost threw up.

I heard a swish and before I could create another thought, that wide thick paddle contacted my plaid pants. The bees from my stomach joined forces with a thousand more and all stung me at the same time, right on my butt where my pants were tightest.

I happened to look up and realize between licks one and two, that Principal Day had a window air conditioning unit in his office. It made a loud rattling sound because the yellowish plastic cover on front was broken on one side and didn't fit over the filter anymore. It was unseasonably cool in his office and it felt really nice, for a split second.

The second lick hurt worse than the first one because it just added an extra thousand bees on top of the first thousand. By the third lick, my butt was numb, and it didn't hurt quite as bad – maybe 500 bees and I didn't notice the cool air or the rattling air conditioner anymore.

"Wait in the hall while I whip Woody," Mr. Day said flatly.

"Yes, sir," I replied with a little sniffle.

I walked out into the hall and sat in one of the two wooden chairs I saw. They were always there, one on either side of his door, backs against the wall, waiting for bad kids to come sit in them before getting licks. I'd never sat in them before and I swore I never would again. I'd won the rubbing contest. Woody had cried during the erasing. I had not.

I stopped sniffling when I heard Woody getting his licks. It was loud. It sounded like the pop of a huge limb when it breaks off a live oak tree. I couldn't believe I'd been hit as hard as he was hitting Woody. Maybe he knew Woody was lying, or maybe my licks were just as loud. My heart had been swishing in my ears so loudly I probably didn't notice. Woody yelled out and I took off to the bathroom before he walked out of the office. I wasn't in the mood to see Woody. I wasn't in the mood for Woody to see me crying.

We never talked about the incident. I wasn't sure if Woody was my best friend anymore.

SIX

"Do you like girls?" he asked.

"Yes," I said.

"You got a girlfriend?"

"No." I wasn't sure what that had to do with anything.

"Do you even know what to do with a girl?" he asked in a sarcastic tone.

"I answer the notes they leave in my trashcan," I said. I'd had a small plastic trashcan on my desk since second grade. A girl would put a note full of questions in the can. I would answer the questions and put the note back in the can. She'd read my answers and we'd stare at each other for a while.

What else would I do with a girl?

I followed him back to his room with the aquarium, and the fish, and the dirty rocks, and the too-small pump.

"I'll teach you what to do when you're older. When you do have a girlfriend."

I didn't understand. But I didn't say anything. He would think I was stupid if he knew that I didn't know. I looked at the aquarium and noticed new little cages in the upper corners where hundreds of tiny, sand-grain-sized fish eggs and baby fish swished around in a big cloud. They were the babies of some of the larger fish that lived lower down in the fake habitat. I traced my finger against the glass where the big cloud huddled.

There were so many. I wondered if I could count them all.

"If the babies get out of the cage the parents will eat them," he said, noticing my fascination with the tank.

"Why would they do that?" I asked, shocked. "They're so little, and helpless."

He shrugged and sat cross-legged on the floor.

The other fish didn't seem to notice the cages, but I was glad they were there. The cloud of little eggs and babies continued to swish around in clockwise circles over and over until they reached the surface. Then they all streamed down the hazy glass sides and started over again from the bottom. I was hypnotized by the continuous circular motion. I was going to ask Mom for an aquarium.

My shorts made a clicking sound and I snapped back to us, sitting on the floor. He unbuttoned them and slid his hand down the front. He asked me to lay down.

"Why don't you get hard like me?" he asked, point blank.

"I don't know," I replied. Heat rushed into my ears and cheeks. My big ears let us both know that what he had just said embarrassed me.

Was I supposed to get hard? It was the first time he'd ever mentioned anything specific about what we were doing.

He showed me his. It stuck straight out like mine did in the mornings when I had to pee really, really bad.

I waited for the game.

Why aren't there any games first anymore?

Is this a game?

Would it turn into a game?

This part didn't seem fun. I didn't like the questions about girls. I had no answers. I felt stupid.

"Wait here," he said. "I'll get something that will feel good, like your girlfriend will when you get older."

My mind raced.

What does that mean?

What could it be?

Maybe some kind of toy.

He came back in with a warm washcloth. Just a washcloth. After removing my underwear, he laid it over me. It did feel better than what he usually did.

"This is how your girlfriend will feel when you do it with her."

Do what with her?

I tried to imagine how a girl would make me feel that way. I pictured a girl putting a warm rag on my naked body to make me hard.

SEVEN

I rode my bike down to the schoolyard. I loved being there on a crisp, blue-sky Saturday morning in the fall, when there were no teachers or multiplication problems or lunch breaks or erasers or principals.

I parked my bike by the chain-link baseball backstop on the corner and walked across the hard-packed dirt toward the perfectly rectangular building with the darkened windows. I tried not to step on the faded chalk lines left over from last week's baseball practices.

As I looked up at the window to our room, I imagined myself in there, all by myself. I was sitting in her big desk. I was drawing on the chalkboard. I was running down the halls. No one could see. No one cared. My steps slowed as I neared the building.

I wrapped my hand around the lowest rung of the fire escape ladder. I knew I wasn't supposed to climb up there, but it invited me up every time I got near. The ladder went up, the slide came down. It was a big, rusty colored metal slide that looked like a round tube that had been cut in half length-wise. Just a big half-pipe attached to a lower one that went the opposite direction, down near the ground.

I sat for an hour or so. My shoulders relaxed as I watched cars driving by and people mowing their lawns across the street. They were oblivious to the short little third-grader perched up on the second section of the three-section slide. I tried to stay still so that no one would see me and make me get down. Butterflies tickled my insides every time I saw a car getting near. But I was hidden well. I was safe. The familiar, wet green smell of the freshly mown grass mixed with the smoky gasoline from the old thumping lawn mower made its way over to the fire escape. I breathed it in.

After jumping down and beginning the short walk toward my bike, I saw an injured lizard. I loved lizards – any kind of lizard. And snakes. And frogs and toads. The lizard looked like he'd been stepped on the day before, or injured by a cat or bird, it was hard to tell. He was a six-lined racer…one of my favorites – dark green and reflective blue, with six yellowish green stripes outlined in black, extending from his head all the way down to his tail.

I was obsessed with trying to catch the little bastards. They always managed to stay just out of my reach. Once, I had gotten close enough to grab one by the tail, but his tail fell off and wriggled in my hand as he made a hasty escape under Grandma's brick wall. This one couldn't use his back legs, so he was an easy catch. I picked him up to take him home and try to fix his legs.

As I got closer to my bike, I looked at the ground and saw a huge bed of red harvester ants. Their bed was as round as a trashcan lid and littered with grass, seeds, sticks, and twigs from nearby yards and gardens. There were ants streaming to and from the mound, along their well-worn paths. Some were going out to look for new seeds and insects, and some were coming back to the mound with goods they had already harvested. The paths were as wide as a piece of masking tape and extended all the way across the schoolyard and down to the street's edge.

The ants looked like dark red lava contrasted against the hard-packed beige dirt as they streamed away from their home. I wanted to take the racer home and help him get better, but for some reason I stopped and placed him in the bed of ants. I watched with a mix of horror and excited pleasure as they swarmed his thin body.

When he tried to escape I pushed him back to the center where more ants were pouring out of two small perfectly circular holes carved into the cement-like dirt. I felt a rush of adrenaline as the ants tore at his soft green skin with their sharp curved pincers. He wriggled left and right, up and down, but it was no use. There were ants covering every little bit of him.

After a few minutes they began dismantling him, piece by piece. Their thick mandibles easily sliced through the small hollow leg bones.

They were trying in vain to squeeze the oversized pieces through the small openings of their mound to take parts of him down to where the fat queen and her tiny white, ravenous babies were waiting.

I snapped out of it. Maybe I could pull the racer out and save him? But, it was too late. He wasn't moving. He was gone. I was horrified, and I felt a kind of shame that was new to me. It burned my belly, and my face, and sent heat through my entire body. I loved lizards and yet I had just put one through the most agonizing death I could imagine.

What the hell is wrong with me?

I jumped on my bike and sped home, crying all the way.

When I walked in the door and Mom asked why I'd been crying, I told her I'd fallen off the fire escape and that she'd been right to tell me not to climb up there.

"I'll never do it again. It's dangerous."

EIGHT

I was freezing as I walked down to Grandma's house in my biggest coat and my black, red-soled rubber boots. I had my long johns on and they were tucked way down in the boots with my jeans. Mom's insulated socks were already slipping off my feet and making me walk funny. My Pittsburgh Steelers beanie with the big yellow ball hanging from a string on top covered my damp hair.

I glanced over to see if he was home as I passed by the house where the games took place. No lights were visible from the road. First, a sense of anticipation. Then, a sense of urgency. It came up suddenly. I had to get to Grandma's. I had to get there now.

The cutting wind bit at my cheeks and burned my nose. It hadn't let up all week. The ponds had frozen over at the farm and the cows couldn't drink. I was headed out with Paw Paw to break the ice, so they didn't die of thirst. I might even get to walk out on the frozen pond and pretend ice skate. Mom said it was dangerous, but it was thrilling to walk out over the water and see the fish and turtles below.

Paw Paw's '72 Chevy Heavy Half pickup truck called Old Blue was out in the driveway warming up. It had a 350 engine with a four-barrel carburetor, four on the floor transmission, a 410 rear end, and mud-grip tires on the back. The blue smoky steam from the exhaust pipe felt warm on my face and I breathed in until my eyes and throat started burning. Paw Paw was waiting in the living room when I walked in. The heat from the floor furnace smacked me in the face as I took off my beanie. He looked up with a smile.

"How's my Booger Boy?" he asked.

"Ready to go," I said.

I *was* ready to go, but I loved being at Grandma's house when it was cold. Grandma had hot chocolate sitting on the table for me. She waited until I sat down and added the marshmallows. I sank into the couch. Safe and warm. Warm and safe. The big furnace cranked out heat from the hallway. When it reached 72 degrees, it cycled off and made a series of loud popping noises.

"Is my big boy ready to go check on the cows?" she asked in her usual sweet voice.

"Yeah," I said.

Paw Paw got up and grabbed his denim jacket. I quickly slammed the last bit of gooey, chocolatey, marshmallowy liquid in the bottom of my cup. I gave Grandma a quick waist hug and sprinted out the front door. When I hit the half-frozen sidewalk, my feet slipped a bit and I took a tumble into the yard. I looked around to make sure no one had witnessed my fall, jumped up, and walked slowly the rest of the way.

I jumped in the truck through the driver's side door and slid over to my usual spot. I loved Paw Paw and I loved Old Blue, especially when he let me drive on the narrow one lane road we called the Cow Trail. I didn't expect to drive today though, not with ice starting to accumulate on the trees and grass, and the sidewalks. It wouldn't be long before the roads got slick, so we needed to hurry.

Paw Paw got in behind me, threw his denim coat on the seat between us and shut the door. That truck was all metal and when he closed the door it sounded like a rock hitting a tin barn. He pulled out his Marlboros and matches. He pulled one straight white cigarette out of the pack and licked the end. He stuck it between his wrinkled lips and put the pack back in the pocket of his soft grey button down shirt. I waited in anticipation for him to strike the match. Maybe he knew I loved that smell and maybe he was playing a game with me, because when I looked up he was smiling and holding the match just short of the rough sandpaper striking edge of the little blue matchbox. He slid it across the box and the sulfur smell of the freshly lit match finally made its way to the smell center of my brain. Now I was ready to take on the world.

As we headed out of town toward the farm, we made a slight detour and stopped at the MKT Railroad depot. All the old railroad men hung out there and it was always bitter sweet to see Dad's truck parked in the parking lot. I never knew where he was, I just knew he was in charge of that big engine while it hauled all of those cars full of rock and coal and oil down the track to parts unknown. The site and sounds of the trains in the yard excited me. The site of Dad's truck made my heart sink a little. He was gone a lot.

Paw Paw slid off the blue vinyl seat and said he'd be right back. He was. After handing out hellos to a couple of retired buddies, he'd grabbed a bottle of Coke for himself and a Dr. Pepper for me.

I knew the routine.

He reached under the seat and grabbed a small flat paper bag with a black cap barely sticking out of the wrinkled and twisted top. He let me drink a couple sips from the Coke and filled the void with the Old Crow Kentucky Straight Bourbon Whiskey from the sack. Not much, just a tablespoon or so, but enough to release that wonderful burning smell into my nostrils and let me know we were ready to be on our way.

We got to the farm and pulled up to the multicolored barn. The rusty corrugated tin panels which made up the walls and roof were dotted occasionally with a shiny new one. It gave the whole barn a patchwork quilt look. The knee-high grass left tiny flat seeds on my coat as I hop-ran toward the big sliding door. We chunked a few bales of hay in the back of the truck. Rust stained my fingers as I removed the figure eight shaped hooks and let the tailgate down, securing it with the attached chains. The soggy bag of range cubes was sagging against the cab when I jumped in the back. This was my favorite part. This was my job. I stayed in the back with the hay and cubes while Paw Paw drove slowly through the nearest pasture. As we putted along I could hear the tires squishing through the black topsoil and when I looked back, I could see the brown chocolaty ruts stretching out behind us. It was wet, and it would be icy tonight. I felt like a man. Just me, in the back, doing all the work.

I strategically pushed a couple pats of hay over the edge of the tailgate every few feet, while simultaneously feeding a steady stream of cubes from the partially tipped range cube bag.

Every now and then I'd reach down and grab a piece of a broken cube and pop it in my mouth. Mom said it was nasty because they contained bull piss, but that didn't much matter because they also contained copious amounts of molasses. And, molasses trumped bull piss any day.

The cows frantically followed the truck, getting so close that they bumped the edge of the tailgate occasionally. Like a swarm of flies on fresh crap, they buzzed around each other trying to gain an advantage, trying to get closer to the source of those wonderful bull piss and molasses range cubes. The cow named Pet always followed too close and tried to get the cubes straight out of the bag. She was a brindle color, purplish brown with vertical tan and black stripes from head to tail. No horns adorned her smooth round head. Her spotted white face contrasted her dark body. Sometimes it seemed as if she might jump up in the truck with me. I wondered what I would do.

When we were done with the feeding, we attempted the drive down to the tank. I knew we couldn't make it across the creek, but I hoped we'd try anyway. The steep banks of the creek were already too muddy to walk, much less drive, and I imagined our mud-grip tires spinning and shooting a rooster tail of mud out behind us for a mile.

It was a long slippery walk to the back tank and Paw Paw decided against it. Instead, we decided to check on the front tank on our way out. We made sure it wasn't iced and got back on the road toward home.

He cranked up the heater in that old Chevy and we made the rainy drive back toward Smithville. I snuggled down into the thickest part of my coat and dozed in and out to the smells of Marlboro, Old Crow Kentucky Straight Bourbon Whiskey, and sweet earthy cow shit. There was no radio and we didn't talk. The windshield wipers tapped the tune of a song I'd heard the day before.

NINE

Mom did all the packing for our trip to the deer lease. I pretty much always wore the same cold-weather clothes. I was still wearing the coat and pants I'd had on with Paw Paw the day before. Mom packed all our food-stuff and Dad loaded the truck with all our bags, guns, coolers, and other miscellaneous camping stuff we'd need for a whole week in the Hill Country.

The terrain changed quickly. My view from the back window had gone from flat grey pastures and skinny cows to rolling hills and colorful oaks and ash juniper. My stomach was churning butter...we were getting close. I was super excited about the hunt. I was a little terrified that he was going to be there. I didn't know what he would do or how he would act around all the other people.

We drove past the Cherry Springs city limits sign and turned off on the small two-track lane that lead to our deer camp. We all jumped out to pee before starting up the hill.

We bumped up the small road, while limbs from overreaching bushes screeched against the side of our truck. We weaved up the hill and parked to the left of the trucks and trailers that had arrived before us. Everyone was gathered around the front of the camp, helping each other get their gear inside before it got dark. A thin line of smoke extended from the old rusty stovepipe jutting from the top of the building.

I saw him immediately. Anxious energy shot down through my

legs. I wasn't sure what to say or how to act. I didn't want anyone to know. He'd made me promise. My mind raced from thought to thought, trying to remember how I'd acted the year before – before the games had started.

He was helping someone with an ice chest. They each had a hold on their end, trying not to trip as they did that awkward sideways, carrying-an-ice-chest walk. He ignored me when I slammed the truck door and walked past.

I was cold and glad that the unpacking went quickly. Everyone was in a great mood because cold weather meant the deer would be moving and the big bucks might still be running the does. Deer hunting was the best. Outside all week. One on one time with my parents. And, I was excited for a chance to possibly shoot my first buck. We all unpacked, humped our sacks into the camp house and got ready to eat some camp grub.

While the adults organized things, I had a look around. The camp house was a one of a kind structure. A tight little stone building, with an old lean-to on one side. Many of the jagged white rocks had fallen from their original places and were replaced with concrete, bricks or wood. It had been used as a stagecoach stop back in the old days. Old rusty square nails and small colorful bits and pieces of antique cups and plates littered the ground.

He still ignored me as I walked around poking at things on the ground. It made me nervous. Our usual interaction would have included some tickling or roughhousing of some sort. I worried someone might notice that we weren't talking. Or, that maybe he would talk to me too much later. I didn't know how I was supposed to act.

I noticed both of my brothers close behind as I trailed further away from the camp house. We began scouring the dry creek behind camp looking for arrowheads. Rocks and roots protruded from the loose sandy banks. Huge limestone boulders had dislodged, rolled down, and were stacked in the bottom in weird statue-like poses.

As I was turning over some smaller rocks near the crumbly bank of the creek, hoping for a spearhead or any other artifact that looked like it could have been made by an Indian, I found something even better. It was sticking out of the weathered limestone and all I could see was the dull grey tip. I knew immediately what it was and made sure none of the other boys were close enough to see as I started to excavate the tiny treasure. It was a bullet. A big bullet. Dad later said it was a .45 or .50 caliber slug, and it was most definitely used in a gunfight, probably to ward off marauding Indians or stagecoach robbers.

I pictured an epic battle just out front of the little stone shack. Indians behind every rock and tree. Cowboys stuck inside with their long rifle barrels sticking out of the few cracks and windows. Puffs of smoke from gunfire. Arrows stuck in the wooden posts of the lean-too and corrals.

I stuck the bullet in my pocket, peed one last time, and went in to eat dinner, or supper as we called it. We ate just before dark. Everyone was eager to get up early in the morning and try to beat the sunrise to the deer stand. Camp fare was better than any gourmet restaurant. Two slices of thin white bread slathered with a thick layer of Miracle Whip, a couple half-inch thick wheels of venison summer sausage, or donkey dick as Dad called it, and a thick square slice of cheddar cheese. Topped off with a Fanta orange soda…The best.

So, it was early to bed. The brick-walled room was so cold that every time I let out a breath, a cloud of condensed moisture rose up from the tiny face hole I made in my covers. There was condensation on the smooth parts of the walls from the heat of our bodies, all closed up in that tiny space. I dozed off long before the last of the twinkling reddish coals went dim in the small potbellied wood stove.

I woke with a start. Everyone in the tiny camp-house seemed to be asleep. Different nighttime sounds came from each corner, and I could tell Dad was by the opposite wall, just by the sound of his snore.

My brother was in the queen-sized bed and so was he. I knew he had arranged it so that I was in the middle, between him and my brother. His hand was heavy and cold on my leg and his fingers felt like icicles. I felt a kind of panic knowing how close we all were. My brother's knee was actually touching my other leg. Somehow it didn't seem right for him to touch me with my brother right there in the same bed with us.

He left his hand on me for a full minute or two. I didn't move. I couldn't move.

Should I move his hand?

Should I get up?

This didn't feel right.

What about my brother?

What about everyone else?

It didn't seem to bother him, so I guessed it was okay. He slowly eased his head under the covers and did what he always did. I tried to pay attention to what he was doing, but I just knew my brother was going to wake up. My heart was pounding. The covers moved up and down and he kept making raspy breathing noises. After staying under the covers for a minute or so, he resurfaced. He put my hand on him and moved it back and forth with his own. Suddenly, he pushed my head under the covers and finished. He didn't normally do that, but it wasn't the first time. After he finished, he went silent for a while and just laid there.

I thought he must have dozed off. But then he jumped up, went outside to pee, came back in, and got back into his warm spot. It wasn't long before his heavy mouth breathing blended in with the others' snoring. I listened to the rhythm and tried to make myself fall asleep. I couldn't. My heart was still beating in my ears. Swish swish. Swish swish. Swish swish.

I couldn't make my eyes stay closed. In the darkness, I listened for signs that my brother may have been awake. Any sounds. Any movements.

Did he see or hear or feel anything?

I must have dozed off for a while because the blaring intermittent buzz of the old alarm clock in the corner woke me.

Where am I?

The lights came on with a click. I looked to my right. He was there. I looked to my left. My brother was still asleep. I didn't want to crawl out of the warm covers. But I didn't want to stay where I was either. He was awake, but he didn't look over. The frigid little room felt like a walk-in freezer.

He finally crawled out from beneath the oversized sleeping bag we'd unzipped and used for a top comforter. The top was green, the lining plaid. The tangled sheets had been pushed down to the foot of the bed during the night's activities.

My brother woke up, crawled out of bed and asked what we had to eat. He showed no sign of having heard anything during the night.

Whew.

I watched him closely, though. How could he have slept through that? The covers had moved. There had been noise. The raspy breathing. I nervously walked around, looking for the socks I'd taken off last night. My stomach felt queasy and nervous. I just knew *that* shouldn't have happened around other people. I wondered if I'd get in trouble if Mom and Dad found out. I kept the bees bottled up in my stomach until we had our guns in the truck and were on our way. No one could know. I'd promised. No one could know.

The deer feeder always went off at daybreak, and Mom and I got settled in the little box stand just a couple of minutes before the world lit up. The stand wasn't much. A square box made of thin splintery plywood. It looked like an outhouse with windows that were cut out at eye level if you were sitting. A loose-fitting door on one side was held closed with a piece of wire wrapped around a nail. Mom sat on a metal folding chair and I sat on a white five-gallon bucket. The raised ridges in the bottom of the bucket, which was the top of my stool, hurt my ass. But as I looked at the cold, rusty metal chair holding Mom up, I knew she had it worse.

The deer were accustomed to the regularly scheduled corn. They showed up early to wait for the free meal they knew would come flying out of the sky. The corn was like candy to them – little on nourishment, big on taste. The feeder was crude. A camouflage 55-gallon barrel that held a hundred and fifty pounds of corn, held up eight feet in the air by three wobbly legs. An electric motor was mounted underneath. The motor had a small spinning plate between it and the barrel. As the corn dribbled out of a small hole in the bottom of the barrel, it rested on the plate. The motor was connected to a battery and a timer. When daylight peeked through the dark sky and the preset timer finally clicked to the right second, the motor spun the little round plate like crazy. The spinning plate had little raised groves which caught the corn and threw it in all directions. The same thing happened at dusk.

As light began to brighten the sky, we could make out a group of does and what appeared to be a buck standing under the feeder. They were finally calming down after being startled by the whizzing motor. Even though it happened every morning and evening, they always seemed surprised. The corn pelting them on their sides and backs was enough to send them into the woods for a few minutes. They were small and skittish. They stared up at the barrel, probably wondering if the feeder would suddenly go off again and if they would need to bolt. It did not.

My feet were as cold as they'd ever been. The three layers of white tube socks I had on inside each boot did not equal one nice warm wool sock. On top of that, my boots felt too small with three socks crammed inside each one, so there was no blood in my toes. None. I knew for sure that they would fall off before we got back to camp. I'd seen it on TV. First, they would turn black. Then, they would fall off. I'd be the only boy in school with three toes on each foot. I shivered inside my oversized camouflage coveralls.

I should have worn more clothes.

Mom looked cold too. Her hands shook as she lifted the binoculars up to take a closer look at the hungry deer. We were a hundred yards or so from the feeder, so it was hard to tell if the deer were bucks or does.

My teeth chattered. They wouldn't stop.

"It's too cold for us to be sitting here without a heater, or something to keep us warm," I said. "We probably won't see anything big anyway."

"Shhhh." She answered.

"Can we just go back to camp?"

"Shhhhhhhh." She lipped silently. "There's a nice buck and some does walking out."

She let me look through the binoculars. After a minute of trying to merge the two black little circles into one, I was finally able to see something.

Whoa. All I could see were antlers. Dark antlers. Eight long sharp points…maybe ten or even twelve. He ran the other buck away and sniffed after one of the does. He stuck his nose right up to her tail and started licking. He squinted his eyes, curled his nose up and stuck his head in the air. It must not have smelled very good. He trailed around behind her with his nose to the ground for a few minutes and then stopped to eat.

Enough corn was scattered around on the ground to keep them occupied for a while, so we weren't in a hurry. I handed the binoculars back to Mom and she sized the buck up for a couple more minutes. She made up her mind and decided he was the one. He was a shooter.

I was so excited. I was also freezing my ass off. My toes were still burning, my face was cold, and I couldn't stop shaking. Cold, mixed with the excitement of Mom potentially shooting the monster buck, was more than I could take. I felt like I might pee myself. I'd had to pee for a while now. I wished she'd hurry.

"Are you gonna shoot?" I asked.

"I am," she answered.

She got the scope just right and the gun settled on the window-sill of the little wood-sided stand. The floor was creaking, and I tried to stop shaking.

"I have to pee," I said. My teeth chattered.

"Shhhhhh," she replied. She was shaking, either from the cold or the excitement of the giant buck she was about to drop.

I wiggled my toes back and forth, moved my feet up and down, and blew into my hands. Nothing worked.

"My toes are falling off."

"Shhhhhh!"

I wished she'd shoot already.

She was breathing hard. I watched her trigger finger. It was moving, ever so slightly backward. Squeezing. Moving. Squeezing.

Boom.

We both heard the WHOP of the bullet hitting the deer broadside. We knew she'd gotten a bullet into him.

Now, for the wait. We both giggled with excitement and I didn't feel cold anymore. The sudden rush of adrenaline I'd felt when she shot that old 6 mm Remington was enough to relieve me of the certain frostbite I'd been doomed to endure just seconds before. We nervously waited the accustomed thirty minutes and got out of the stand to track the deer. Good thing, as I'd just started to get cold again. I still had to pee.

I loved tracking. Dad taught me how to track critters when I was five or six years old, and now that I was eight, I was pretty much an expert. We found blood and hair from the shot right away, but it was mixed with bloody corn. The tiny bits of corn were mixed with partially digested leaves and grass and had obviously been chewed and swallowed. That meant the shot was a little further back than perfect, and probably into the guts. Not good.

We tracked him for a hundred yards or so. A tiny red drop here, a hair or two there. A little frozen blood smeared on tall grass. A wobbly hoof-print. Then, the blood ran thin. Another few yards and it disappeared.

We searched and looked and searched some more. No blood. No hair. No chewed corn. No nothing.

Dad showed up a few minutes later.

"Heard you shoot," he said excitedly. "What did you get?"

We lead him back to the last area we'd seen blood. Once he had a sense of which way the buck was running, we fanned out in that direction, walked a zig-zag pattern, and looked for more signs, or maybe if we were lucky, a dead deer. I scanned the ground for any tiny red specks or smears that we may have missed earlier. No luck. We looked around for a few more minutes and Mom suddenly yelled.

"I found him."

We all gathered around to see the trophy. He was piled up in the thick brush underneath a medium-sized oak. His neck was bent back on his body and the exit wound was definitely a little far back, in the guts. He had frothy blood on his mouth and nostrils. The rest of his blood was in a huge black pool on the ground beneath him. Mom and I looked down at the buck and then immediately looked up at each other. It was a tiny little buck with only four points—a young fork-horn. That was not the deer we'd seen through the binos. That was definitely not the deer Mom had shot.

"That doesn't look like the buck I shot," she said.

Dad said that one of two things must have happened. We both had "buck fever" and thought the buck was huge just because we saw horns. Or, the small buck had walked in front of the larger buck while Mom was messing with the scope trying to get him in focus. I could tell by the tone of his voice that Dad thought it was buck fever. He just figured that we imagined him being bigger than he was.

I felt my ears getting hot and I knew my face was red. I walked in the woods behind the stand so that no one would notice that I was embarrassed. I didn't want them to make fun of me, or Mom.

I know how to hunt and track.

I knew I hadn't had buck fever. Buck fever was for babies. The buck we saw was a monster. He was huge. This was not the buck Mom shot. I'm not sure Dad believed us, but he never said anything else about it. Mom and I knew the truth.

We got back to camp and showed everyone the buck. After hearing the story, the camp was split fifty/fifty on whether Mom and I had been the victims of a bad case of buck fever, or if the small forky had walked out in front of the bigger buck at just the right moment and taken the bullet. No one was sure, except Mom and me. Well, Mom had been shaking pretty bad right before she shot, but I was pretty sure it was because she was cold. It pissed me off that they were laughing at us and didn't think we knew how to hunt. Either way, the deer had to be hung and cleaned.

Dad had gutted him in the field, so we hung him from the hanging tree near camp to let him bleed out for a while. As I'd watched Dad gut the buck before, I couldn't help but notice the similarities between field-dressing a small fork-horn whitetail buck, and pretend field-dressing a small eight-year-old boy.

After the excitement of Mom's trophy died down a bit and the day began to warm, we looked for something to do. There were hundreds of wooded acres for us to roam and the last thing we wanted to do was sit around camp. We looked for more arrowheads, and it seemed the other boys were all looking for a bullet. The one I'd found before had become the object of more than one envious stare. I'd planned on keeping it a secret, but I'd bragged about it instead. I reached down to my right front pocket and felt for the outline of my bullet. Still there.

TEN

Us younger boys took off down the creek and thought we might find some frogs or snakes to harass. It was still cold, but who knew, as the sun rose maybe they would be out trying to soak up enough warmth to stay alive another day. As we were focused on the crust of ice coating the smooth rounded rocks around the few puddles remaining in the creek bottom, we heard something rooting around in a thicket just over the bank. We all froze.

Deer? Coyote? Bobcat? Employing our best stalking techniques, we eased up the crumbly bank. The dry crispy Live Oak litter made it almost impossible to be quiet. I looked at the others and told them shhhh. Whatever it was might hear us and bolt before we even got a look.

We shimmied over the lip, our heads peeking up from below the edge in a row. Peering through the blonde stiff stems of some leftover grass, we saw movement. There he was. A long pointy snout was rooting through the leaf litter and softer dirt underneath. A leather like shell seemed to flex every time he moved. We all focused on the most important part…his tail. It stuck out of the back of his shell. Stiff white hairs stuck straight out, from its base to its pointy tip, and were highlighted by the slanted sunlight coming through the mass of tangled vines and small Shin Oaks. That tail was the key. We all knew what to do. Someone sneezed.

His nose came out of the leaves and his short-necked head rose as he leaped into the air. He bounded away on powerful hind legs, just like the kangaroos I'd seen on TV. Dust and rocks flew out behind us as we scrambled the last foot over the bank and ran after him like a pack of wild dogs. We hooted and hollered. We snorted and yelled. We laughed and farted. Staying as close to him as we could, we knew what he would do. We'd done this before.

He finally swerved left, jumped over a crumbling dead Live Oak and dove into a small dark hole. The hole wouldn't have been visible had we not seen him duck into it. We gathered around and caught our breath, waiting for Josh to finally straggle up. We had the dillo where we wanted him, now what?

One of us had to reach his hand down in that dark hole and grab the end of that rough callused tail. Mom said armadillos carried leprosy, so no one wanted to touch him. Someone older had usually done the dirty work. I was the oldest one there, so I guess that's why I finally volunteered. I didn't want to look chicken in front of both of my brothers. The hole looked deeper now. I was sure black widows had nests in every crack and cranny, all the way down to where he was hiding. What if there was a rattler in there too? I was about to call it off.

"I'll do it," Luke said. His chest was puffed out and he was acting brave.

"No one's going to do it if I don't do it," I answered.

I reached in, barely able to tell the difference between the tail and the many roots protruding from the gravelly sidewalls. I touched it. He let out a low, menacing, pig-like grunt. I touched the tail again. Another grunt. I steadied my hand, closed my eyes and reached further into the darkness. I grabbed the tail near the base and pulled back as hard as I could. He didn't move. I reached in with the other hand and strained against the bug-eyed little shit. He started to give. When I began to gain some ground, he grunted louder and more frequently.

All of a sudden, he popped out of the hole and tried to bounce away. I held tight. He bounced and bounced. I yelled for Luke to grab him with me, but the shelled little bouncer was making me twirl around in circles as his heavily clawed back feet dug into the earth and he kept trying to bound away. Each time his feet touched the ground, he jumped and shot gravel and sticks and dirt everywhere.

Luke got a hand on the tail and slowed the dillo down. I was able to lift him from the ground, just enough to keep his feet from digging in.

Every once in a while, he'd get a foot on the ground and spray us with dirt and leaves. But he was ours. Now we just had to figure out what to do with him.

Nine-banded armadillos were pretty common in the area and especially common around our camp house. We'd usually catch one and show him off for a while, then let him go. When we got close to camp, some of the older boys took interest and started tossing around other ideas. I was wary about letting them have him. We'd killed them before with our .22 rifles or slingshots, but I'd never caught one by myself. I didn't want this one to die. After the ordeal he put us through, it seemed he deserved to live a little longer.

We had the dillo tied to a tree with a small piece of rope. He was just relaxing by the trunk. He didn't seem too upset, and probably had no idea what was about to happen to him, but the older boys had hatched a plan. They had some paint and decided the scaly looking little fella's natural defenses weren't quite up to par. I watched as they began applying an army green base coat to his shell. A couple boys shook their cans—different colors, of course. After the green, they added black, brown, and grey spots. The normally grayish armadillo now sported a completely new camouflaged paint job. He matched most our deer blinds.

To top it off, they added a couple of Lone Star beer stickers from the sides of some bottles. Before releasing him, they pressed the stickers on to the wet paint - one on each side. He now resembled the Lone Star beer mascot we'd all seen hundreds of times on commercials and delivery trucks everywhere. They removed the knot from the rope and off he went. No one saw him again. I could only imagine the face of the surprised hunter who first saw that little Lone Star dillo pop out of the woods.

The second night in bed was a repeat of the first, almost exactly, including the clutching fear that we'd be caught. On the third and final night, he shortened things up and just used my hand. I was startled when his stuff spurted out on my arm. It usually went on his stomach, so I didn't know what to do. He left me lying there when he got up to pee and I surely couldn't ask him how to clean it off. I just stayed there with my hand suspended above the bottom sheets, but below the top covers. Panic spun through my chest and I looked over to make sure Luke was asleep.

I didn't want any to get on the bed, or someone would surely know what had happened. They'd know what I'd done. A giant invisible fist squeezed my insides and tears welled up in my eyes.

What if Luke wakes up?

I was frozen in place.

What's wrong with me?

I need to do something.

I slid my feet up to my butt, so that my knees created a tent with the covers. That way, my arm wouldn't touch them.

After he was back in his warm spot and his rhythmic breathing turned to snoring, I slipped out from under the covers. Easing the door open and sliding out into the full moon glow with only my stark white long john bottoms for protection, I froze while pacing around the front of the camp-house trying to figure out what to do with the gluey mess still stuck to my hand and arm. I hadn't put on my long john shirt for fear of getting some on the sleeve. There were a jillion stars in the sky and the high, full moon made it feel almost like daylight. It was bright and clear, and a super hard freeze was underway. A roll of paper towels down by the hanging tree caught my eye, so I walked in that direction.

As I plodded I could feel the cold penetrating my thin holey clothes. I wished I had that shirt. The ground crunched under the weight of each step. I'd hastily slipped my boots on without socks and was now regretting that decision. I was sure my feet were freezing to the inside of the thin leather. If anyone came out, I wasn't sure how I was going to explain why I was down by the hanging tree in my long johns with sockless feet inside my boots. No one could know about the stuff on my arm or how it got there. He'd told me not to tell. I hadn't. I wouldn't. Ever.

The stuff was cold and stiff by the time I reached the tree. I wiped at it, but it didn't all come off. It just smeared and became stuck in my arm hair. I looked for water, but it was all frozen. I thought about using a Coke, but I figured they were all frozen too. I couldn't go back to bed with him stuck on my arm like that. If anyone saw it, they'd know what it was. The only thing left to do was rub dirt on it and hope it would come out of the fuzzy blonde hairs.

I rubbed and rubbed and rubbed. The cold black dirt and tiny white rocks felt like freezing sand paper and broken glass on my arm. I rubbed some more. I finally decided the only way to be sure it was all gone was to pluck out any arm hair that his stuff had touched. I pinched my fingers together and yanked at a small bunch. The hair mixed with the gluey mess came out with a fiery rip. It was cold. My arm already hurt from rubbing it with icy dirt and rocks. The pain of ripping out the gluey mess-covered hair was more than I could take. I felt the tears streaming down my face. I made sure I didn't cry loud.

I sobbed quietly, while ripping the last bits off of my arm. The tears seemed to freeze halfway down my face and I wondered if I could get frostbite from frozen tears. I pictured myself with permanent scars from my eyes to my chin and everyone laughing at me because I'd been crying.

Even with just the moonlight, I could see how red my arm was. I wasn't sure if it was just irritated or if maybe I'd rubbed hard enough to make it bleed. I used a couple of the paper towels to wipe off the dirt and any left-over gluey mess I might have missed. Icy prickles stung my arm as I walked back to the camp-house and got a chunk of ice out of one of the coolers. I rubbed the clump of cubes on my arm until it became a little numb and I thought I might be able to go to sleep. I dabbed at my scratched up, hairless arm with the used paper towel.

What was I going to do with the paper towel? I couldn't leave it on the ground. I couldn't put it in the trashcan inside. I couldn't leave it out on the table. Someone would notice what was on it and start asking questions. They would surely know.

I walked back down to the hanging tree and grabbed a decent sized piece of wood I found lying off to one side. I started scratching at the half-frozen ground. After a few minutes, I placed the pieces of dirty paper towel in the small cat hole I'd created and put the loose soil back on top. I stomped and stomped it until it was as flat as the surrounding ground. When I was sure it didn't look conspicuous, I placed a few leaves on top and called it good. I looked back once as I walked back to the camp-house to make sure the burial spot wasn't noticeable. I wiped at the dried icy tears with my other arm and slowly opened the noisy door. My spot was still empty in the middle of the bed next to him. I walked across the room on cold feet and slid back under the covers. My spot wasn't warm anymore.

He didn't stir. My brother didn't stir. I stared at the lone beam of light shining through the tiny crack above the leaky wooden doorframe. I was tired. I wanted to go to sleep. My arm hurt.

We packed up the next morning. Most everyone at camp had been successful and everyone would be taking home some meat. I didn't get my buck but was lucky enough to be with Mom when she got hers. Only one hunter hadn't bagged a deer, so everyone pitched in and gave him some venison to take home. It could have been any of us. All of the hunters had been in the same situation before and it wasn't a big deal to give up a little meat.

As we bumped down the road towards home, I thought about Mom's buck, the old bullet I'd found, and the armadillo we'd caught. I thought I'd be more excited about the trip. I tried to remember the details of our hunt. My eyes went down to my arm. The scratched spot was still pink and sore.

Somewhere along the way, Mom asked about it. I told her the truth – I'd done it down by the hanging tree. I felt guilty about not telling her the whole truth. Something inside told me not to.

We all unpacked our black trash-bags of smelly deer lease clothes when we got home. Us kids took turns jumping in the bath. That first bath back from the deer lease was the best. I loved the smell of the Suave shampoo as I lathered it up on my thick mop. Watching the water transform from clear to cloudy brown – I didn't know I had that much dirt on me.

It was going great until the soapy shampooey water hit my raw irritated arm.

Oh yeah…the gluey mess.

The cold boots. The scratchy dirt. The arm hair pulling. The ice cube rubbing. The staring at the ceiling all night wondering if he'd wake up and spurt on my arm again. The way he didn't ask me about my arm the next day. I didn't feel clean in the bath anymore.

ELEVEN

Christmas was usually my favorite holiday, but this year I hadn't asked for
anything spectacular from Santa. Partly because I had a suspicion he wasn't
real. A mix of fear and sadness gripped at my chest when Mom asked us to
make our Christmas lists. Mom and Dad had no idea about my doubts and
I didn't want to tell them. But, when they tried to use Santa as leverage for
me, or my brothers to act right or stop fighting, I wasn't quite as committed
to being good as I'd been in years past.

The year before, I'd found the red Magic Marker on the TV. The
exact same color red that Santa signed his gifts with. None of the other gifts
were ever signed with red Magic Marker. Only Santa's. It must have rolled
behind some bric-a-brac, or one of the many family photos sitting up there.
When I saw the Marker, and then looked at Santa's red signature on every
gift from the North Pole, I felt a punch to my gut. I was confused.

Why would the big guy leave his Marker at our house?
How would he sign presents at everyone else's houses?
Why would he even sign presents at everyone else's houses?
Why would he sign presents at our house?
Wouldn't he sign them all at the North Pole?

I wanted to ask but I wasn't sure I really wanted to know the
answer. This year, I was going to wait up to see what Mom and Dad did,
and just what the hell was going on.

On the big night, they tucked us in and told us we'd better get to
sleep soon, or else Santa would pass over our house. I rolled my eyes and
let out a huge sarcastic breath. We didn't even have a chimney, and I knew

51

Dad locked the front door. If there were a Santa, how would he even get in?

I laid there quietly for a while and stared at strange figures created by streaks of moonlight on my square white ceiling tiles. I watched the oak limbs make dancing shadows on my curtains as the wind blew them back and forth and in crazy circles. It was a blustery cold night outside and I was glad to be tucked in my warm covers, with only my usual face hole exposed to the outside world. I heard Dad checking our rooms to see if the coast was clear. I'd finally see what really happens on Christmas night.

I heard whispery noises in the living room—Mom and Dad's muffled voices and shuffling feet. I strained my ears as they giggled and snuck out the front door, quietly jingling the keys to Mom's big gold Chevy Suburban. They cranked the behemoth up and backed it out of the driveway. When I heard them accelerate down the street, I sprinted through the living room and slid on pajama knees to the window of the front door. I watched through the left vertical side window, just beside the door, barely making a crack in the already bent one-inch metal slats of the mini blinds. They didn't see me. They were already heading down the street.

The mini blind chord rubbed my cheek as I watched them drive down the block to Aunt Nancy's house and pull in her driveway. Was she going somewhere with them? They both got out and went inside. I strained my eyes. The streetlight glinted off of the shiny square objects as they toted them out into the freezing wind a few seconds later and began piling them into the back of the Suburban.

They spent a few more minutes getting the rest of our stash from her place, then jumped in and drove the gifts with the shiny red special Santa wrapping paper back to our house…one block. I ran back through the living room, and slid feet first into my bedroom. I watched from the dark crack on the hinged side of my door, as they carefully placed each item under the Christmas tree. Mom signed them all with Santa's beautifully unique signature. Santa always had such great cursive handwriting, always done in large, beautiful lettering with a wide, red Magic Marker. The S was tall, with great curves on top and bottom and a long sweeping tail that slid under the rest of the letters but didn't connect to them.

My mind raced. I felt betrayed.

Had Santa ever been real?

Was this some kind of off year?

I knew it wasn't. I knew in my gut the moment I'd found the Magic Marker the year before that Santa wasn't real. Confusion. Anger. Sadness. Anger. Confusion…because what I was witnessing still didn't quite make sense to me. Anger…because they'd lied to me since I was a baby. Sadness…because Santa wasn't real. Anger again…because I'd been stupid enough to believe that a fat man in a red suit flew around in a sleigh pulled by flying reindeer and then squeezed down people's chimneys to put presents under a dead tree that they'd cut down in the woods and hauled into their house.

Mom and Dad may have hidden our presents down the street at my Aunt's house every year. I wasn't sure if they'd wrapped them at our house and then took them down there all at once, or if she did all the wrapping for them. I was sure of one thing – Mom had great cursive handwriting, with beautiful lettering. She made the best S I'd ever seen.

On Christmas morning, we opened Santa's presents.
Santa's presents, HA.
We had family over and afterward we went to some of their houses for the usual eating and drinking. Even though there was always drinking, Christmas and New Year seemed to ramp things up. Mom and Dad, and most of our friends and relatives, drank beer at all the functions – birthday parties, wedding showers, weddings, funerals, church picnics, baby showers, fish fries, Bar-B-Ques, fishing, hunting, camping, and pretty much any other occasion that came up. But Christmas and New Year brought out the good stuff, whiskey. Those magically shaped bottles that my uncles brought over, with that awesome burny smell, made me want to taste them all. It was the same smell I knew from Paw Paw's small bottle of Old Crow Straight Kentucky Bourbon Whiskey.

It was a good smell, but I'd never tasted it. I'd only had a couple sips of beer in the past from random relatives' cups. I'd also accidentally gotten drunk at a party a couple years before.

My older cousin was at our house, with his mom, dad and two sisters. He had something dark and bubbly in a short clear glass. Ice jingled as he swirled it around and took a small sip. He held it under my nose.

"Want some?" he asked.

It smelled like Dr. Pepper. Little bubbles bounced on and off the top of the brown liquid and went up my nose when I breathed in.

"It smells burny," I said.

"You a little chicken?" he asked.

I assured him I was not.

I took a big swig, downing almost half of his glass. My throat constricted, and I tried hard for my next breath. He grabbed it back.

"You'd better be careful," he said. "This stuff is for grownups. Coke is for kids."

He may have been eighteen, but he didn't act like a grown up.

TWELVE

The holidays were over. I had to go back to school, and without any more breaks to look forward to, I knew it would be boring and overall pretty shitty. The months between the holidays and summer felt especially tough. I loved all the Thanksgiving and Christmas activities we did in school just before the break, and when we had to come back, I felt a huge let down. No more drawing and trading presents and nice teachers.

Last year we'd learned multiplication and division, and Woody and I had erased a hole in the top of our hand. We weren't best friends anymore, but we still hung out on the playground. Our friend Arthur was an artist and he drew cool pictures of anything we wanted. Woody folded a piece of notebook paper a thousand times until it was a tiny walky-talky with moveable parts, and an antenna. Arthur drew cool Spiderman pictures on the tops and bottoms and we had the coolest toys on the playground.

We had to learn to write 1979 on our papers. Ms. Robinson yelled when we wrote 1978. We'd been writing 1978 for a whole year and it didn't seem fair to be put out into the hall just because we weren't used to writing 1979 yet. I got it down pretty quickly. Woody sat in the hall a bunch. One day Ms. Robinson yelled at Woody. Woody told Ms. Robinson what he thought about 1979. He had to go visit Mr. Day. He came back crying, and he wrote 1979 on his papers from then on.

Icy winds and dry leaves hung around throughout January and into the early spring months. Once it finally began to warm up, I couldn't wait to get home from school and mess around the house or ride around the neighborhood on my bike. I rode my orange bike everywhere. I loved the black banana seat and high curvy handlebars with black rubber grips. One of the neighborhood kids had traded his rear tire for mine, and now I had a wide racing slick on back. Dad was mad because he said the racing slick was worn out and didn't have much tread left on it. He wanted me to get my other tire back and I said I would. I didn't try too hard...I loved that racing slick.

I got home from school on a brilliant spring afternoon and moseyed my way down to the river. I went down the small goat trail we'd made on the big hill behind our house, carefully stepping, sliding, stepping, sliding. My bare feet finally found the bottom and I squished along the crooked edge, down near the water. The trail down there was always wet and muddy. Coon and possum tracks were left in the soft muck as evidence of nighttime activities down near the waterline. I was on the lookout for snakes, frogs, toads, lizards, or whatever else might be crouched or hidden along the muddy grassy area between the water and the upper bank.

I sometimes spent hours down there, many of them without Mom and Dad knowing. Mom said we shouldn't go down there without a grownup or we might fall in and be drowned by the current and if we got caught up in the current we'd die. I wasn't afraid of the current as long as I wasn't in the water.

I hadn't been walking long when I saw the green and brown markings of a Southern Leopard Frog, barely visible through some thick grass on a tiny knoll. His shiny wet skin gave him away and he didn't know I'd seen him. I eased over and crouched behind him. He was perfectly camouflaged, except for the slight shine I'd caught when I glanced down from just the right angle. Easing my arm around the clump of grass, I swiftly slapped my hand down with a high arching motion. That way, if he jumped in mid swing, I still had a chance to catch him in the air. I came up with a wriggling mass of grass, mud, and frog. His long legs and webbed feet flailed around wildly and splattered mud on my pants and coat sleeves. He pissed wildly into the air in hopes that it would cause me to drop him. It did not. I talked to him for a few minutes after walking out and sitting on the neighbor's small boat dock. I was out over the water but felt secure because it was deeply anchored and made of stainless steel grates, not to mention that the dock had made it through the last couple floods with only minimal damage. I wasn't overly concerned with dying in the river's current. But Mom's words still rang in the back of my mind.

Startled.

I didn't expect to see him down here. I really hadn't seen him since the last day at our deer camp. His blue corduroy FFA jacket and bell-bottom jeans stood out against the greens and browns of my sanctuary. He walked toward me, but I didn't think he saw me. I sat out near the end of the dock with my legs dangling over, my stubby toes barely touching the water. The dock was five or six feet below the bank and unless he looked down he wouldn't see me. I unintentionally glanced down at my arm. The red was gone, and the hair had mostly grown back.

My first thought was to hide. I didn't know why. I just didn't feel like talking to him or playing any special games. I also didn't feel like skipping the games and having him use my hand to help him spurt his gluey mess all over my freshly grown arm hair. I didn't want him to see me, so I sat still, hoping he'd just walk on by. I dropped the frog in the water. His scissor strokes carried him down into the murky depths and after a few seconds, out of sight.

He stopped at the top of the trail that led down to the dock.

"What are you doing?" he'd seen me.

"Catching frogs," I didn't look up. "Bout to go home."

"Want to walk down a little further and help me check coon traps?" It was a little warm for trapping coons.

"Sure," I jumped up. I loved trapping coons.

He had a couple of traps set a little further down river from our property boundary, toward where Grandma and Paw Paw's property came down to the river. He used live traps, so the coons wouldn't gnaw their own legs off trying to get out of the old steel leg traps. Plus, sometimes they'd catch a neighbor's cat or dog, and using steel traps would have messed them up pretty bad.

I'd been out baiting the traps with him before, and my job was usually to hold the sardines, and try not to eat them all before we used them in the traps. We slipped and squished through the mud down close to the water. Turtles scooted off their logs and silently slid under the still water as we walked by their favorite basking spots. Frogs launched from the bank, sounding their loud, high-pitched yip just before hitting the water. I wondered how much further we'd have to walk.

We stopped at the first empty trap. It was tied to a dead log that extended out over the river's edge. The bark had sluffed off one side and fallen into the water. The log looked as if it could crumble and wash away at any moment. There were obvious signs of animal activity. The top of the log was well-worn from the bank to the water's edge, where all the little padded feet and sharp claws had made their way to and from the great vantage point on the end. They could sit there and survey the muddy spot below, waiting for unwary frogs or crawfish to swim or step into striking range.

He didn't have any bait. I hadn't noticed earlier. When I asked him about it, he said we were just going to check the traps now, and that he'd come down later with his special potion of sardines and cheese and re-bait them. After walking through chest-high grass to the second trap, we stopped for a breather. I raked small wet seeds from my arms and reached down to pick a couple of beggar's lice off my pant legs. He said he had to pee. He turned his back and I could hear the pee splattering onto the already saturated ground.

When he turned back around, he still had it out and it was sticking straight up in the air. I was shocked to see it in his hand, right out on the bank of the Colorado River. He slid his hand back and forth and asked me if I'd help, so that we could get to the other traps faster. He was sure there was a big coon in the next one. I didn't want to touch him out there where anyone might be watching.

"No." I said.

He didn't say anything else.

I flushed with embarrassment as he finished himself off with a few more violent strokes. I'd never seen anything like that. I could only stare. He left his gluey mess right out on the log, right next to the place his trap was tied. He squeezed the last little bit out, wiped his hand on his pants, and put it away. He didn't talk, and we didn't check the rest of the traps.

I wondered if there might really be a big coon caught in the next trap. Panic started to wriggle in my stomach. Would it starve if no one checked? I pictured the shiny coon pacing in the trap, looking for a way out. I wondered if the gluey mess would keep a coon from getting into this trap. I wondered if it would keep a coon from walking out to the end of the log to catch a frog or crawfish.

Had he thought about any of those things before leaving me on the riverbank and walking back up to the street?

My mind raced. The panicky little bees worked their way from my stomach, up to my chest. I didn't want him to know. I would come back down later and find that next trap. There might be a big one in there.

THIRTEEN

My ninth birthday party had come and gone, and it was almost time to start
back to school. Summer was almost over and our third week of hundred-
degree temps was coming to an end. The street was hot and the yard was
brown. Dad had just mowed the dead grass, mostly because of the tall
weeds, and red dirt was visible in the bare spots. I was sitting on the porch
swing staring at my bare feet when he came strolling up.

"You wanna go out to the farm and do some fishing?" he asked.

"Yeah," I said, trying not to show how excited I really was. We'd
fished out there before, and I knew there were huge bass in those tanks.
We'd fished quite a bit that summer. Over the last year we'd spent a lot of
time together. I hung out at his house. We went fishing and bird hunting.
We'd checked coon traps down at the river and out at the lake. I had just
turned nine and was smart enough to know that when he asked me to go
fishing with him, it usually meant going fishing…plus the other thing I
knew we'd end up doing. The routine was the same almost every time. No
more long, drawn out games. Just shorter versions of the games we'd
played when I was younger, or no games at all. It was summer. It was
normal.

I loved fishing and I jumped in the front seat of the big long car.
The seat was hot and my legs burned for the first few minutes, as we sped
through the neighborhood. We rumbled out of town and headed for the
farm. The car was big and wide and long. It rocked up and down as we
went over the curvy, humpy, rollercoaster road with the windows down and
the radio blasting.

We swerved in through the gate of the farm and headed back to my favorite tank. It was not the biggest, but the water was deep and stained black by the tannin from a million oak leaves that had fallen in over many winters. The bank near the front was clean for the most part and only a few reaching strands of Bermuda grass extended out into the water. Scattered clumps of spiked rush grew along the edge. There were water lilies along the north side and I'd caught many lunkers from the murky shadows beneath their pads.

But I had my favorite spot. I made a B-line for the narrower part of the tank. An eroded gravelly drain fed the west end during rain events and had created a deep channel. The water was deep and dark, with stumps and limbs poking up and breaking the surface all the way across. The trees reached from the depths, their ghostly limbs trying in vain to sprout leaves and regain the life they had before they were flooded. Colorful fishing lures…blue, green, black, silver, new and old, dangled from the limbs – a testament to the skill it would take to get the lure in the water, in just the right place, and pull a giant from back there. It was worth the risk.

We fished for hours and loaded our stringer. We threw a couple of the smaller ones back and put the rest in five-gallon buckets with a little water, hoping they'd make it back to town.

As soon as we got back to his house we started cleaning the bass. He was going to let me take the ones I caught back home with me but told me we'd just clean them all right there on the side of his garage first. He had the perfect place to clean fish and I didn't mind putting all the guts in their trashcan. Dad wouldn't mind that either.

After thirty minutes or so, we had them all finished and bagged up. The sun had dropped and I could hear the whee uuur whee uuur of the cicadas letting me know that it would be dark soon. He said he was heading in to eat supper and I should probably get home before dark.

I was confused. Maybe I'd done something wrong. He'd rarely let me leave without some version of one of our games. I walked home with my head low, wondering.

What did I say or do?

Is he mad?

I hope he's not mad.

I hope he won't stay mad.

I sure like when he takes me fishing.

FOURTEEN

The weekend after the fishing trip, he called me over. I was speeding by on the orange bike with the cool racing slick, when he yelled and asked if I wanted to play some Frisbee. Excitement shot through my legs as I spun the bike around and hopped off, just before letting it crash to the ground near the curb. I tried not to act surprised. I'd moped around for the last few days thinking I'd said something stupid.

Whew, he's not mad.

Or if he had been, he wasn't anymore.

We played Frisbee in the yard for an hour or so. It was fast and fun. Running. Catching. Diving. Sliding. The grass was wet from a recent shower and the air was thick enough to taste. Frisbee turned into tackle Frisbee and when I tackled him I noticed his shorts were unzipped. I was embarrassed and I looked around to make sure no one else had noticed or happened to be looking our way. Maybe he had been walking around like that all day. I tackled him, he tackled me and we both got thirsty. He offered water and we headed inside.

We sat down on the big couch in his living room, right inside the front door. It was much cooler inside. I had scratchy green grass stains on both knees from tackling and getting tackled in the wet carpet grass. It was bright and the shades were slightly open. Thousands of green pecans hung from the limbs in the front yard, causing them to sag all the way to the ground. They still had growing to do, but it looked like fall would bring a bumper crop. Webworms had created dense spiderweb-looking masses all over the pecan trees along the street. They'd need to be sprayed.

He immediately took his shorts all the way off and began showing me what he wanted me to do with my hand…but I already knew. He liked to show me each time. I was moving my hand to his requested rhythm when we heard a car door slam in the front yard and voices walking up to the house. He jumped off the couch and sprinted toward the bathroom, knocking a *Sports Illustrated* off the coffee table as he went by – Bjorn Borg had won his fourth Wimbledon title.

His brothers walked in and gave me a surprised look. They hadn't expected anyone to be there, especially me sitting on the couch by myself. The TV was off.

"What are you up to?" one of them asked.

"He's in the bathroom," I said. "I'm waiting on him to play more Frisbee in the front yard."

They didn't bat an eye. I watched as they walked over to the kitchen and poured a cold glass of punch, some Ritz crackers and cheese. They chatted about nothing for a few minutes, while they finished up their crackers and tossed the empty box on the counter. After guzzling a second glass of punch, they filled their empty glasses with water from the tap and downed them. They grabbed what they came for out of the other room and left, not noticing the magazine on the floor, or the panic in my eyes.

I waited for a few minutes. The buck in the corner looked down on me. His brown eyes never let me know what he was thinking when I sat on that couch, but I felt like he always knew what would happen. He knew the secret.

Nothing was said when he came back in. His shorts were still off and it was still sticking straight out. He put my hand back on him and showed me the rhythm for the second time. It only took a few seconds for him to finish. He cleaned the gluey mess off his stomach and the bottom of his t-shirt with three or four tissues from the yellow box on the coffee table. He went to the bathroom and peed loudly for a long time. After releasing all the water in his bladder, he came back in and chugged two full glasses from the kitchen tap.

We went back outside and played Frisbee. Running. Catching. Diving. Sliding. That was a close call.

FIFTEEN

I could feel the sweat on my top lip but resisted the overwhelming urge to wipe it off. I knew everyone was looking at me. Why had I picked that shirt for the first day? I loved cars. But we weren't in little kid elementary anymore. We were in Sam Houston Elementary. Fourth grade. No one else had a car on their shirt. I knew everyone thought it was stupid.

I thought I'd heard the bell ring but no one was moving. I knew everyone from last year, but they all seemed older and I didn't see any of my friends.

Where the hell is Woody?

The bell rang out and echoed off the houses across the street. We squeezed through the front door of that old two story red brick building like cattle being herded through the shoots at auction. Dust rose. Sweat flew. Hair was pulled. And I'm pretty sure the boy next to me wiped snot on my shirt. It was chaos.

I didn't know where to go. This was the first time we weren't going to be in the same class, with the same teacher, for the whole day. We had to find homeroom, and then we'd have to find all of our other classes when the bell rang, at different times throughout the day. I didn't even know where my homeroom was.

After going to the wrong class and hearing the snickers of some of the girls and boys I'd had in Ms. Robinson's class the year before, I finally found my homeroom. Only a few familiar faces. Who were all these people? Woody wasn't there. They all stared. I was late.

I sat down and listened to the homeroom rules, and before I could

64

write down the last two, the bell rang. Chaos again. Everyone jumped up and sprinted out the door. I followed the mob of sweat and snot out into the hallway. I looked left. I looked right. Panic again. Where was my second period class? I had to go to the office to find out.

"Why didn't you take your schedule home and learn it like all the other kids?"

I didn't know. I'd been to the school with Mom and Dad and gone over all of it, but I couldn't remember where anything was.

I couldn't wait for the lunch bell to ring.

I'd been walking around the halls of Sam Houston Elementary all morning and hadn't made it to one class on time. Everything felt big, noisy and fast. I'd brought my lunch, so I just decided to sit out on a table in the shade of the building. The playground was a mix of grass and dirt and there were kids milling around everywhere. The ground was dry. Dust kept drifting up onto the table and I tasted it when I opened my mouth to take a bite of my sandwich. I saw familiar faces in each group of swirling, sweating kids, but didn't know what to say. I couldn't think of anything.

Hey guys.

How's it going guys?

What're you up to guys?

Stupid. All stupid.

So, I sat and ate my lunch, hoping no one noticed me until the next bell rang.

When it did, I pretended to be busy. Arranging, folding, and rearranging the empty sandwich and chip bags in my lunch box. I acted like I didn't care that the bell rang or that everyone was headed to class.

The chaos of the morning repeated itself. I waited until all of the other kids rushed in, and then slowly walked up the stairs after. I wasn't in a hurry. Fourth period. I had no idea where I was going.

Stupid.

It stuck with me all day. Kids walked in front of me with their arms around each other. Others seemed to be sharing lockers. I felt alone. Confused and alone.

The last bell finally rang and I bolted through the side door, made the quick three-block walk home...and cried. I never wanted to go back. I said as much as I pushed the squeaky porch swing back and forth with one foot.

"It'll be okay," Mom sad. "Just keep going and it'll get better."

"It won't." I stared up into the limbs of the big elm.

"You'll be able to talk to all of your old friends."

"I only saw a couple of them today." I remembered all of the strange faces staring at me in the halls.

"You'll remember how to get to class," she finished. "It'll all be fine."

My shoulders slumped.

"I wish Dad was home."

But he wasn't. Dad was *out*. That's what we called it when he was at work. He had no regular hours on the Railroad and he could be called out at any time. I loved it when he was home. But, he missed games, parties, and other important events because of that Railroad. This time he'd been gone for three days. I hated the Railroad. I knew it was a good job and that my Paw Paw had done it too, before he'd retired. But I hated it. Fourth grade was so terrible. I wanted to tell him bad, but I had no idea where he was. He was out.

The big elm was waving its crazy arms in the wind. I felt a little better after Mom went inside. She'd closed the door softly and left me sitting there for a while. The big tree always calmed me. I didn't have any homework, and probably wouldn't for the rest of the first week. The teachers said we needed time to get used to finding our classes and stuff, and I was sure they were talking to me.

"Stay out until supper," Mom had said.

That meant until the streetlights came on. I jumped on my orange bike. It had a new back tire. The racing slick had blown out when I hit a rock in the alley across the street the weekend before. Dad was right. It didn't have much tread.

I turned my bike into the wind and pretended to shift gears as I built up speed. The road sloped away from the house and down toward town. My tires hummed and the sprocket sounded like a fishing reel as I sped down to the old Central School.

The handlebars dug into the sandy dirt of the empty playground as I bounded off my ride and slid to a stop. For once, I was glad to have shoes on my feet. A few steps toward the building and I hoisted myself up onto the fire escape. I was tracing the cracks in the old peeling paint with my finger when the sound of the janitor closing and locking the big old

66

windows startled me. I wondered what would happen if I snuck in and sat at my old first grade desk in Ms. Frank's class. She had been my favorite teacher. She'd let me take home all the decorations from her walls when school was out that year. I'd taken a little poster with the letter B from the cursive alphabet lined up along the top of the walls. It had a beautiful B and a bear. I loved bears.

I didn't love my new school though. Sam Houston Elementary was too big, too loud, and I hated having to go to all those classes. My hands started to tremble a little just thinking about it. Even though Ms. Robinson hadn't been my favorite teacher, I missed her class. I missed sitting next to Woody. I missed multiplication tables. I missed the one Kraft American Single that Mom stuck between two pieces of white bread for my lunch. I missed going to Mr. Day's office for rubbing a hole in the back of my hand with an eraser. I missed getting in trouble with Woody. I missed the twins putting notes in my trashcan. I couldn't have a trashcan in fourth grade. There were too many classes.

As I was walking back to my bike, I saw the giant red ant mound where I'd killed the injured lizard. The images came back to me with a rush and I felt the heat in my face and ears. I remembered the helpless, colorful little guy who needed my help. I'd killed him. I'd killed him in the worst way possible. The ants had torn him up, in little pieces, bit by bit, slowly. My stomach churned and I thought I might throw up. I had to get out of there.

I jumped on my bike and took off. I was only supposed to go as far south as Highway 71. It was the main road between Austin and Houston and sometimes it was really busy. There was only one red light, at Main Street, and it didn't slow traffic down too much. I looked both ways...twice. I knew I wasn't supposed to cross. I could see the red light two blocks up, on my right. No cars.

I bounced up on the right pedal and took off. I dodged a gravelly pothole, turned left and rode past Ken's Pharmacy and Western Auto. I made a U-turn, doubled back and parked in front of Winn's Grocery. I leaned my bike against water-stained bricks on the front wall of the building and walked in. The smells from the candy aisle made my mouth water, even though I knew I wasn't going to buy any. I craved the tangy strawberry Now and Laters. I loved the way little bits of the tangy sweet squares stuck to my back teeth and how I could still taste them an hour later.

I walked all the way back to the fish. There were three small dingy aquariums, and each had different kinds of little fish swarming from end to end, trying to make their way out to open water. I sat down in front of the one on the right and watched the little sharks swim back and forth against the glass. As I watched those little zebra colored fish – the ones with pointy orange fins, I thought back to the noise of the sad little pump and the dim light in his room that first time. They darted up, down, left, right, chasing each other from one end of the aquarium to the other.

Where's he been lately?

After leaving the store, I walked my bike down the cracked sidewalk toward the very end of town. A huge wad of pink shiny bubble gum was stuck to my front tire. A little bit of it stuck to the concrete each time it touched the ground and left tiny gum strings waving in the air. I could smell the sugary sweetness and wondered if someone had dropped it by accident.

The railroad tracks glinted in the sun. The twinkling light bouncing off the steel tracks gave the illusion of a stream or lake and seemed to beckon me toward the end of town. I stopped in the side parking lot of the depot. The old wooden building was alive. I could smell the warmed-over coffee and hear the sounds of old men talking. The floor creaked as someone walked from one side to the other. I loved going in with Dad or Paw Paw and laughing with all of the other Railroad men about some trip on some train to some far away sounding place. I sat and looked at Dad's truck and wondered when he'd be home. I didn't dare walk in and ask. They'd think I was just a stupid kid.

I was about to ride up the same road I'd coasted down but decided to take the narrow alley all the way back home. It was bumpier and took more time, but it was also more fun and it went right behind his house. I rode through puddles and over grassy planting strips. The water spewed up on my face and slung off the back tire and on the back of my shirt, as my tires parted the shallow muddy puddles for a brief second.

Will he be home?

He'll be home.

I just know it.

I scraped by metal trashcans with my legs and may have heard one or two fall over behind me. I didn't look back. My elbows brushed the tall hedges and boxwoods reaching up and over the chain link fences, guarding the line of white square houses against nosey eyes and ears. I jumped every road crossing and ditch. Something squeezed my insides, just a little. I was bored, but it was more than that. There was a sad kind of restlessness just below my skin.

I ended up in the alley behind his house. I hadn't planned to stop. I hadn't even thought about stopping. But, I did miss it. The games. The excitement. Him. Maybe we could play Frisbee or something. I knew he'd want to if he saw me. I knew he'd want to if we talked and joked and laughed.

I let my bike fall to the ground near the trashcans, like I always did, and opened the back gate. The smell of the freshly mown yard filled my nose. There was a loose carpet of grass clippings on the sidewalk leading from the gate to the back door. They were wet enough to stick to the bottom of my bare feet and it felt kind of like wearing socks. I'd have to wipe them off when I got home.

My face and ears began heating up as I tried to figure out what to say when he answered the door. It had to be something funny. Something cool. The first knock was so quiet I could barely hear it myself. Embarrassed, I knocked again. The third knock was even louder. I waited. Frisbee. Deer hunting. Wrestling. Which would it be? He liked the deer hunting game best, so I thought about just asking him if he wanted to play that.

He didn't answer. No one did. We hadn't done anything cool since that summer weekend we went fishing. And we hadn't played any games since the weekend his brothers had almost caught us.

Maybe he doesn't want to play anymore.

Maybe he found someone else to play with.

Maybe I did something wrong and he's mad at me.

Loneliness crept up behind me and wrapped its arms around my chest. I missed the fishing and deer hunting and Frisbee. Hanging out with him made me feel important. Fourth grade sucked. I wanted to feel big and cool, even if just for a little while.

I moped my way down the alley and back toward my house, leading the bike along beside me. I kept it steady with one hand on the left handlebar. When I let it go, it rolled straight for about three feet, but then I had to catch it and get it going again. As the shade of the big elm engulfed me and my bike, I knew I'd made it home. The bike landed where it always did. I jumped back on the swing and resumed my rhythm. I wasn't even sure why I'd gone riding.

I didn't sleep well that night. My mind was caught in a tornado of the same thoughts I'd had after knocking on his door.

What's wrong with me?

Why doesn't he want to hang out with me anymore?

Did I do something?

Did I say something?

Does he think I'm stupid?

Did he find someone else to play with?

I had no answers, just swirling thoughts. Round and round, one after another, keeping me from drifting off. But at some point…I did.

Next morning I was up at daybreak. I crept into the woods behind our house and crossed to the other side of the fence. There was no wind and the air was heavy with humidity. Drops of amber colored water held tight to the ends of the Spanish moss dangling from every tree. I was going to kill something.

I wasn't sure what, but I knew I could rely on the old Benjamin Franklin pump action .22 caliber pellet gun to do the dirty work. It had open sights and a natural wood stock. The wood on the lower part of the stock was ribbed and rounded, worn smooth by years of handling and use. I pulled out on it and slammed it down to pump up the pressure for firing the deadly lead projectile that waited patiently in the chamber. I usually only pumped the handle ten times because Dad said we would damage the air cylinder if we pumped it more than that. Today I pumped it twelve. I wasn't taking any chances.

I was looking for birds and squirrels. Birds were preferred because it never took as long for the ants to devour them. But I'd off'ed the occasional squirrel too. Either one would do today. I felt empty and hollow and mean. I didn't know why, but it didn't much matter. I knew I'd feel better after shooting one of my feathered friends and watching the ants do what they did best. They had a way of ripping and tearing the anger and hollowness and meanness right out of me.

I crawled under some vines and looked up. There was movement in and out of a green briar thicket just ahead. The mass of vines and thorns was situated just below the first horizontal limb of a huge Live Oak. There were other scraggly limbs and vines in the tangle, but the green briar was most noticeable.

The tiny green bird was barely visible among the shiny green heart shaped leaves. He never seemed to stop long enough for me to get a bead on him. It looked like a Ruby-crowned Kinglet, the prize of the neighborhood. We called them Chee Chee Birds. We hardly ever encountered them, and when we did, we could barely see them. It was the tiniest bird we hunted and the hardest to kill. He jumped and flitted and wouldn't sit still for more than a half second.

I laid down on my belly and felt the leaves crunch under me. I was directly below a pointy-leaved shrub. The tips snagged at my shirt and tickled the skin between my shoulder-blades. Sweat ran down my forehead and into my eyes. I thought about the times I'd been crouched under the shrubs at his house…the times he'd hunted me.

But now I was the hunter, and I had my prey in clear view. I waited patiently, just like Dad had taught me in the deer blind years before. The little kinglet settled, then jumped, then settled, then flitted up into the oak limb. Damn! He finally flew back down and settled on an exposed piece of vine between two large leaves. I steadied the old Benjamin. I breathed in and exhaled slowly.

Stay there…
Don't move…
Pow!

A puff of greenish gray feathers let me know I'd been on target. I eased up off my belly, plodded down the hill a few feet and looked at the bloody mass of feathers and beak lying directly in the center of the thorny tangle. I only had to reach in once to know it wasn't a good idea. Green briar thorns were curved, up to a half an inch long, and this one had done its job well. The scratch was deep and about three inches long, from the back of my arm to the middle, and my sleeve was ripped.

I found a long stick in the gulley to the left of the tangle. Delicately, I eased it in and hooked the pointy end around the back of the little bird. I started pulling him toward the opening near my feet. It seemed a shame that his feathers were getting all dirty. I pulled him through the natural slot and stared for a while. His eyes were closed and his tiny beak was just barely open. I could see the pointy miniature tongue attached to his bottom beak. I was sad for a second looking at the dead bird, but I closed my hand around it, gently scooped it up, and started up the hill.

The pulsing red carpet waited. I moved close, careful not to put a foot into one of their trails. The consequences of that mistake had been very unpleasant last time. I found a big, flat, yellow rock nearby and placed it about two feet away from the ant bed. I knelt down on it, and very gently placed the little green kinglet into the middle of the swarming sea of red. There were so many ants that they covered up the little bird and I couldn't see what was happening. I moved him around with a stick, but every time I did, the red swarm covered the newly exposed side, and hid their gruesome work from me.

I felt a sense of disappointment, and a little bit of panic. A small wave of nausea made its way through my stomach.

Why did I shoot my favorite bird?

Why did I shoot any bird?

Again?

Why did I want to watch ants tear him apart?

Why was I disappointed that I couldn't see them do it?

What's wrong with me?

Sweat began stinging the new cut on my arm. Just a faint electric tingling…and for some reason my disappointment was gone. Something in that pain calmed me. When the drop of sweat had touched it, and I felt the initial burning sensation, my breathing slowed. My thoughts slowed. The panicky heartbeat in my ears slowed. I forgot about the bird.

SIXTEEN

After a few weeks learning the new system, fourth grade didn't seem so bad and I loved some of my new teachers. But, I still liked weekends best.

The sun had already gone down and a thousand cicadas were singing their songs in unison…whee uuur whee uuur. The early fall days were getting shorter, and I knew I only had a few minutes left to beat those streetlights home. Mexican Free-tailed bats had already made their trip from nearby caves and bridges and were circling the block. They flew from street light to street light waiting for the bright glow that attracted their favorite foods. The raised pink whelps on my skinny white legs were a testament to just how many mosquitoes we had around our neighborhood, and why those bats chose to come back evening after evening.

I rode my orange bike at top speed up the bumpy asphalt hill from the old elementary school playground to my house. My hat blew off my head a couple blocks from our driveway, and the circle-back to pick it up had probably cost me the all-time speed record from Central School to home. No matter, I made it just in time. The streetlights came to life just as I crashed my bike into the yard. I made it to the front steps in two bounds. Looking back, I noticed that the left handle bar had dug into the ground and caused it to flip end over end and almost land on its wheels.

As soon as I hit the top step and jumped across the welcome mat, I knew it was going to be a good night. The smell of chicken-fried deer steak, boiled yellow squash and cheese, and buttery mashed potatoes hit my nose just outside the screen door. The screen slammed behind me.

"Don't slam the door," Mom yelled, as I slid across the living room carpet and turned the corner with a wide grin.

Mom had her back to the room and was busy mashing the last stick of refrigerated butter into the creamy potatoes. There was a pile of thin, crispy deer steaks on the stove. The flimsy paper towel she'd placed over them to ward off flies and hungry boys didn't work, and I grabbed a small end that was sticking out, only visible to the trained eye. My mouth watered before the salty breaded meat hit my lips. I took a first chew…and instantly regretted it.

As soon as my teeth clamped down, a stream of molten hot juice squirted against the roof of my mouth and the back of my tongue.

Mom turned around when I yelped.

I two-stepped over to the fridge and grabbed my all-time favorite beverage – ice cold milk straight from the carton. I fumbled with the folded cardboard spout and had just gotten it open. I knew I wasn't supposed to drink out of the carton, but I figured I'd probably get a pass in an emergency like this.

"Don't drink from the carton," Mom said.

By this time, the burning had mostly stopped and I just grabbed a glass from the cabinet. The thin orange Plexiglas window vibrated when I let the cabinet door slam behind me.

"Don't slam the door," Mom said again.

The ice cold milk washed over the burning spot in my mouth and I smiled at Mom. I grabbed a plate and sat down at my place at the table, wondering where everyone else was.

"You'll still have to wait because Dad is finishing up some welding in the shop."

The hitch on the cattle trailer had broken and he was fixing it so he could take some calves to the auction on Friday. He must have gotten home while I was playing down at the old school.

Dad finally washed up and my brothers filed in, sitting to my right and left. Mom and Dad sat across from each other toward the other end of the table, and my year old baby sister was on the end in her high chair. I surveyed the table and the distance between me and each dish.

Mom said, "Bless us oh Lord, and these thy gifts, which we are about to receive, from thy bounty, through Christ our Lord…" Halfway through the Amen, the chaos ensued.

We'd all been glancing sideways at each other while Mom was

blessing our gifts, which I assumed were the steaks. There were three growing boys at that table, six people, total. There were seven steaks on that plate. There were always seven. Beverly would only eat a couple bites and that left two whole steaks for whoever cleaned their plate first. You couldn't get more meat until your plate was clean. It was our unspoken challenge...or maybe just mine. Who would finish first? Who would get an extra steak?

I'd become an expert at out-eating my little brothers. I was nine. Luke was seven. Josh five. They didn't have a chance. I had a strategy and it usually worked. As soon as I heard the A in Amen, my hands moved. It was like the quick-draw in a gunfight. I cut my meat in large pieces as soon as it hit my plate. I moved the squash to the side and dipped an oversized piece of tender venison in my mashed potatoes and shoved it in my mouth. I chewed twice. Swallowed. Repeat.

The dripping yellow butter helped lubricate my throat and the meat and potato mixture slid down without a hitch. I even doubled up the last few pieces. I could feel them slow when they got down to my Adam's apple, but they made it through and slid the rest of the way down to my gullet.

The squash was soft and went down smoothly. I shoveled the thin, droopy cheese-covered wheels in, three or four at a time. I forcefully clanged my fork on my plate, just so there was no doubt that I was done. I reached out and grabbed my second steak. Now I could sit back and watch as my two younger brothers battled for the last one. I already knew Luke would win, but Josh was getting closer and closer, as he got older. Luke edged him out by a bite or two and quickly grabbed the spoils from the plate in the center of the table. Josh looked on with disappointment but was comforted with some of the yummy breading left behind by all the grabbing and forking. He seemed content with the salty crumbs and I was glad the battle was over.

I sat back with a victorious grin and looked down at my plate. My trophy steak sat there waiting for me to devour it with the same gusto I'd displayed a few minutes before. I looked up to see if anyone was noticing my victory stare around the table. No. Everyone was busy finishing up their squash and potatoes. I looked down again. The steak looked huge. I wasn't very hungry.

SEVENTEEN

I was standing there with my brother waiting for Dad to hurry up and get down river and pick us up. He'd put the boat in the water under the Highway 71 Bridge and was hauling ass to get to us, so we could put some lines in the water before it started to recede. The river was up due to heavy rains the previous couple days. The boiling tan water was just below the neighbor's dock, lapping up through the rough aluminum grates near our feet. It wasn't very cold, and when the water rose like this, the fish would bite like crazy.

Even though we were going fishing, my mood was grey. It had been grey for a couple months. I'd had a realization since that day in the alley behind his house. Our friendship was over. He hadn't come around. He hadn't flagged me over to play football or deer hunter or anything. I'd done something wrong.

I sat on the big log next to my brother and the dock and looked downriver.

Did he ever come back and check those traps?

Did a big coon really starve in the trap that we hadn't checked that day?

I'd meant to go back and check it myself, but I hadn't. I didn't want to see him down there like that again. I wondered if the gluey mess had ever washed off that log? My ears and face warmed and I knew they were turning red. I hoped Luke didn't notice. I eased my right hand up and traced the outline of the cut on my left arm. It was there, as it always was now. I smiled and relaxed.

I heard Dad coming, as the buzzing of the old outboard echoed off the dense cover on both sides of the bank. The motor let out a rumbley gurgle as he backed off and cut it sharp to his right.

Dad had gotten tired of cussing our old Johnson, so now we had a new-old 20-Horse Evinrude. He was pulling right up alongside the dock so we could step into the boat without having to jump.

A nervous rush of electricity rushed up my legs as I took the first step. I knew if I fell in and the current grabbed me, I would die. Mom's stories were never far from my mind when I was on the water. The boat's rolling wake finally caught up and when it hit the bank and dock, it splashed up through the steel grates and shot water up my pant legs, but only to my knees. I didn't mind having wet socks and shoes. I was on the river with Dad and that was about as good as it could get.

I could feel my mood brightening as we stepped in the boat. It rocked up and down from its own wake. I sat in the front and Luke sat in the middle. Blue smoke puffed out of the motor and hung just above the water's surface. Dad turned the throttle on the long skinny steering handle, we took off with a start. He turned the boat down river and we were heading to his few favorite yella holes. It felt a little more dangerous because yellas tended to hang out in swifter water. Unlike the lazy eddies where we placed the channel cat lines, we'd be braving the swirling deeper areas where we knew the fifty-pounders lived.

We only put out five lines. Each of them was already rigged with eight or ten evenly spaced hooks, each attached to the main line with a short twelve-inch leader. They were all wrapped around an old antifreeze jug, so all we had to do was unwind them, bait them with perch and get them in the water. Dad would drive us downstream of the desired spot and then turn the boat back upstream. He deftly maneuvered us into the swift water, right below a huge storm water drainage pipe. There was still swift muddy water running from the end of the pipe. That pipe always scared me. It was big enough to hide a mountain lion or coyote or the boogey man. But this spot always produced.

I tied the upstream end to a stout willow limb and we began floating back toward the other tie off point. Dad tied the downstream end and we went back up and started putting on perch. Luke frantically grabbed the darting spiny perch from the five-gallon bucket and handed one to Dad and one to me. I stuck the 7/0 circular hook through the perch's back, just below his dorsal fin. He started flapping like crazy and I knew I hadn't hit his spine or any important nerves. He'd be alive and kicking when the big yella swam by. The line burned my hand as we slid back to the next hook. Dad did his best to keep the boat idling at the right speed so I wouldn't have to grab hold, but this was swift water and every now and then I felt the burn.

All the lines were out and Dad pointed the boat back upriver. It was late afternoon and we wouldn't be checking them again until dark. The boat slowed and Dad asked me and Luke if we wanted to drive.

"Yes," we both said.

I got to go first. When the river was up, it could be tough to dodge all the floating logs and debris washing downstream. Luke and I were both smiling because we loved to drive that boat and it made us feel grown.

The Evinrude was mounted to the aluminum boat with two built-on screw clamps. The top of the motor was just about head high and I could see behind us while I was driving. Forward, neutral and reverse were achieved by pulling or pushing the sliding metal handle located on the closest side. The throttle was built onto the long steering handle extending from the motor to the driver's seat.

I pulled the shift forward and heard the grinding click as she engaged. We bumped forward and Dad said to get going. The black rubber throttle squeaked as I turned it counter clockwise. We were off. I only twisted the throttle half way because I was scared to go too fast. But as we gained speed it still felt like we were doing a hundred. The wind blew across my face and made a funny whistling sound whenever I opened my mouth to talk. The old blue Evinrude purred like a kitten as we skimmed the top of the water all the way up past our house to the old sunken bridge. I angled far to the left to get around the remnants of the old Main Street Bridge. It had fallen years before and created a hidden underwater hazard for those who didn't know the river like we did. Jagged metal and concrete were waiting just below the surface, reaching up for the sunlight they'd never quite see. Dad always said that many an outboard were laying down there next to that old bridge. I never even got close.

Luke took his turn and had his own hazards to avoid. Just below the new bridge, where Dad had parked his truck, there were shallow rocks extending across the entire width of the river. The flat grey piece of rock-covered land jutted out from the south bank. It was visible when the river was low and tiny rapids were created as the water bubbled and churned over and through the many edges. There was one tiny slot, all the way to the right where a boat could slide by when the water was low. The slot was bigger that day and the rapids had disappeared because the river was up. Luke made it over the rocks and all the way to the bridge. We let Dad take it from there. He grabbed the handle, got us close to the bank and we both jumped out.

Our bare feet squished in the fishy smelling mud as we made landfall. I kept a tight grip on the long yellow rope while Dad went up and got the truck. As always, the current tried to take the boat down river, in the direction we'd just been. I held fast as Dad backed the trailer in the water. He jumped back in the boat, cranked the motor and quickly drove her in a half circle and aimed for the trailer. He must have been a bit off, because he quickly turned made another half circle and brought her in. I attached the big metal hook from the trailer's rope and started cranking the boat all the way up to the front. The winch clicked as I turned and when the front of the boat touched the trailer I couldn't crank it anymore. She was on, and we were headed home. I high-fived Luke. It was good to be us. It was good to have a Dad like ours. It was good to drive a boat.

With the truck windows down and a cool breeze on my face, my thoughts jumped back to him. Back to my friend. Back to the riverbank. Back to the gluey mess. Back to the many fishing trips. Frisbee. Deer hunting. Wrestling. Naked. Touching. All the things he liked to do. I wondered if I was still his friend. I wondered what it all meant. Was it really over? My thoughts circled about, stirring up little bits of confusion here and there. I knew it was. The thin slice on my arm tingled as the wind made my sleeve flap up and down, in and out. It was over. I didn't know why…but somehow, I was sure now that it was over.

EIGHTEEN

My knees hurt. I'd been kneeling on my little padded bench, just to the right of Father's big throne for what seemed like an hour. My buddy Simon was supposed to serve as altar boy that night, but he was at home sick, or so he said. No one liked doing the Wednesday night mass.

St. Paul's Catholic Church was beautiful, especially after the remodel. The Virgin Mother and St. Paul both wore fresh coats of paint. Jesus looked as miserable as ever hanging from the huge wooden cross above Father's throne. The cut on his side looked fresh, and the tiny droplets of blood running from his hands were so real.

The crown of thorns always made me look away. It was a brutally realistic representation of what a crown of thorns would look like, and I could only ever look at it for a few seconds. Guilt crept in when I felt the material of my sleeve rub the fresh cut on my left arm. After the sharp green briar had sliced me during my hunt for the little green Chee Chee bird, I'd kept the cut alive. It was there. I didn't know why, but it had to be there.

The sleepy Wednesday night crowd consisted mostly of elderly Catholics who weren't crazy about the hustle and bustle of the Sunday services, or folks who were going to be out of town for the weekend and just wanted to get a little praise in the bank before leaving…just to make sure.

Mom always said it was imperative that we go to church every Sunday or we might end up a little short on the day we stood before St. Peter and those pearly gates. God and St. Peter didn't seem to care so much when Mom had a reason to miss…like being at the deer lease. But when one of us kids wanted to stay home…well, no.

Dad only went to church on special occasions like Christmas and Easter. I was always afraid that someday he'd end up staring the devil down, across a pit of brimstone and lava, but it didn't seem to bother Mom. I assumed there was some special arrangement that I wasn't aware of.

I knew every word of the mass because I'd been an altar boy since second grade. It was always the same, and Father never missed a beat. He'd greet the congregants and they'd all confess to almighty God, and to their brothers and sisters, that they had sinned in their thoughts and words, in what they had done, and failed to do. Then they'd ask blessed Mary, ever virgin, all the angels and saints, and their brothers and sisters, to pray for them to the Lord their God. I'd always look out under my brows to try and locate the real sinners. I looked for anyone with guilt on their face or the ones that stared at the floor the entire time. They were hard to find on Wednesday nights, among the bent over little old ladies with pulled back white hair and dark, homemade knitted shawls.

I knelt there and felt like a sinner. It wasn't something I could put my finger on, just a deep down feeling that no matter what I did or how many times I went to church or how many masses I served as an altar boy, I was going to hell. I cussed sometimes, secretly wished bad things on people, and occasionally lied to my parents. I had also killed lizards and birds in the ant bed and had done the same thing to some grasshoppers and other insects. I did have a few more recent sins, too, and I knew they would be on the top of St. Peter's list. Simon and I had served the week before, and I was sure God and Jesus and the Virgin Mother and the Saints Paul and Peter all knew what we'd done with the body and blood of our lord Jesus.

I knelt and stood and knelt and stood and thought about the bony fingers of the devil around my skinny fuzzy forearm as he led me down a dark tunnel toward the light. Not the bright white light that my friends would experience, but a glowing orange and red light at the end of a long dark tunnel…deep down in the center of the earth. I shivered, just as everyone said Amen.

That past Sunday, Simon and I had both arrived at church a little earlier than usual. Thirty minutes was the normal amount of time we usually needed to prepare the holy water, the little bread wafers and wine, and get our robes on. We did this stuff out of habit, along with anything else Father asked us to do before he went back to his room to get ready for mass.

Simon looked at me and said to follow him back to the little room to the right of the church. It was kind of a storage area where everything was kept and where all the smells of mass came together concentrated in one little room. The lingering snuffed out waxy smoke smell from the prayer candles. The spicy smells of the used and unused incense from the Christmas masses. The vinegar and sour grape smell of three empty bottles of cheap alter wine, sitting upright on their little shelf, next to the unopened bottles, which would be sacrificed for this week's services.

I turned around and Simon was holding a bunch of the little round unleavened wafers in both of his cupped hands. I was a little shocked. He had the body of Christ in his hands and looked like he was about to eat it.

He flipped the first wafer up in the air like a quarter and it landed on the fat part of his tongue before he sucked it in and swallowed it.

I pictured one of those cartoon frogs jetting his tongue out and eating a fly.

We both laughed, but when he asked me to eat a couple, I paused.

He knew what I was thinking. "The wafers don't become the body of Christ until Father blesses them," he said.

"Oh," I replied.

We ate the whole box.

He grabbed each empty bottle of wine and turned it up, hoping Father had left a stray drop or two. No luck. He grabbed one of the full ones and smiled.

When he tossed it to me, it was so unexpected that I almost missed. I could just see the broken glass and dark wine spreading on the floor beneath my feet.

What would Father say?

What would St. Peter say?

"Stop it man," I said. "Let's get shit ready for the mass."

He didn't move. Suddenly, he unscrewed the top of one of the other bottles and took a couple of huge swigs. The bubbles from his mouth seemed to get stuck in the skinny neck of the bottle and then release all at once. It made a glunk glunk sound just as he pulled it down. He wiped his mouth with a sleeve from the dark robe hanging on the wall next to us. He stared at me with a crooked smile and handed the opened bottle to me while I involuntarily handed him the full one I'd been holding.

I held the dark bottle in both hands and noticed the pictures of red grapes on the white label. The bottle said St. Paul beneath some French looking words I didn't understand. I'd never noticed that.

"The wine is the same as the bread," he said. "It isn't the blood of Christ until Father blesses it."

I just stood there with my mouth open, not knowing what to do. Simon was only one year older than me and I knew what he was expecting. I'd never tasted wine. I'd never tasted the blood of Christ, which wasn't really the blood of Christ because it wasn't blessed yet. I'd never done anything wrong in church. I'd never done anything wrong as an altar boy.

"You chicken?" he asked.

I assured him I was not.

"Take a big gulp," he said. "It'll taste nasty if you only take a tiny sip."

I turned up the bottle of the almost blood of Christ and took two large gulps, just like he'd done. I swallowed hard – twice. It was dry, and my mouth puckered as if I'd just taken two gulps of vinegar from a pickle jar.

I had to spit, but dared not spit on the church floor, even if it was just the little storage room on the side where no one actually prayed. I opened the door and hocked a big dry pinkish loogie out to the bottom of the three shallow concrete steps. I barely missed the silver pipe handrail on the side. Father was strolling down the thin sidewalk between his little house and the church. He had a black notebook opened across both hands and was studying it intently, without ever looking up. I ducked back inside.

What are we doing? This is church.

We put everything back in its place. I hoped the blood of Christ tasted better after Father blessed it.

After that day, Simon and I regularly feasted on bread and wine – unblessed, of course.

Each time, I knew we were sinning. I justified it by comparing the sin to the bigger sin it could have been, had it already been blessed. I was sure I could pray it away, though I surely couldn't confess it away, since Father was the one that heard all the confessions. Guilty thoughts bombarded me during every mass, but I just couldn't bring myself to confess. I sometimes felt my face flush when I was around Father. I felt like an imposter in that church. I shouldn't have been there.

Maybe Father knows.
Maybe everyone knows.
God surely knows.

When Simon and I were serving the same mass, I sometimes giggled when watching Father hand the body and blood of Christ to the congregants. I was immediately flooded with guilt…every time. He'd give us a sideways glance if we let a snicker slip out.

I helped Simon mow yards and had sleepovers at his house almost every week during the summer of fourth and fifth grades. He got paid to mow yards, and when I helped with the cuttings or leaves he'd give me a dip of wintergreen Skoal.

We started off with the little cottony pouches full of spicy mint concentrated nicotine goodness and then moved up to the long cut. Long cut was just that – wintergreen soaked tobacco cut into long grassy strands. When I placed it between my lip and gum, or "cheek and gum" as the commercial said, it pretty much caused an instant jump in my pulse. Even the smell of wintergreen made my mouth water.

NINETEEN

I hadn't had a close friend since the Frisbee, deer hunting and the other stuff had stopped. Since Simon was a year older, I felt cooler when I hung out with him, almost like before. I considered him my best friend.

We hung out at the kitchen table trying to get out of the summer heat, and away from the flies. The used-up fly strip hanging near the window above the sink twirled in the faint breeze. There wasn't room for one more fly, and the way it moved when the wind came through the screen, made it look more like a decoration than an insect trap.

Simon's mom eased across the kitchen and slid a bowl of vinegar and salt-soaked cucumbers onto the table. I didn't like cucumbers, or vinegar. But I loved those salty little wheels. She cut them so thin I saw right through them when I held up my cucumber John Denver glasses. I slid one into my mouth and the lip puckering taste offset the cucumber taste just enough to make me want more.

Lane finally showed up in the early afternoon. He'd just walked the half-mile down the hill from his house to Simon's.

"Y'all ready for some camping?" he asked excitedly.

"Yep," we answered in unison.

He slapped me a high five and all three of us squatted down in a three-person semi-circle on the living room floor. After a couple minutes of strategizing, we came up with a plan.

"We need to hurry," Simon said.

Our camp was going to be a little further back than usual so we needed to find the perfect spot and get our tent set up before dark. Simon and Lane fought over the last two cucumber slices while I tried to explain the general area of our new campsite to his mom.

"Be careful and don't catch each other on fire," she said. She was only half joking. We always took at least one gallon, and usually more, of gasoline camping with us to start our fires. We never had small campfires. And sometimes we came back with burns or melted shoes.

The black wooden screen door slammed behind us.

"Don't slam the door," his mom yelled.

We went to the little shed beside the house and gathered the rest of the supplies. Our tent, gasoline, matches, buns, wieners, mustard and the little black AM radio wouldn't all fit into the cardboard box Simon's mom gave us. We divided up what wouldn't fit in the box and headed toward the new spot. The pig pens were extra smelly because it was extra hot. They were directly behind the house and we had to walk through them to get where we were going. The ammonia and pig shit smell seemed to penetrate my clothes and I wondered how we'd all three smell in that small two-man tent we camped in.

The pigs didn't seem to mind us cutting across their territory, so we avoided the wallow and crossed the back fence. I placed my foot on the bottom strand of barbed wire and pushed down, while pulling up on the second lowest strand. They both ducked under and held the wire for me. One of the sharp barbs nicked my arm as I was standing up on the other side. Goose bumps tingled my skin from elbow to fingers. I smiled.

The weather was still cool at night so we had also brought sleeping bags and a candle. The candle didn't provide much heat, but made it seem warmer in the tent under a cold night sky. And besides, if the battery in our flashlight went out, we'd need light to look at the Playboy that Simon had taken from his oldest brother's room. Simon always had something from his older brothers. Entertainment for the last campout had been a bottle of liquid condom. None of us were brave enough to put it on our wieners, but we had a lot of fun letting it dry on our hands and creating finger rubbers.

We got everything set up and had our wood ready for the night's bonfire. We had exploring to do before we'd come back, light our fire, start telling stories, talking about girls, and listening to 55 KTSA on that tiny black radio. Simon's family only lived on a few acres, but there were large pieces of property bordering them on all sides. It seemed like we could roam forever, like camping at a national park. I was high. High on nature. High on the thought of a cold night around the fire. We laughed and made fun of each other as we finished up around camp and took off.

We immediately headed west, for the back. The property was triangular shaped and we knew we were getting close when the opposite fence angled toward us. We crossed by the big post. All of the good creeks, tanks, and woods were located across the fence, any fence. After pushing through the rusted barbed wire boundary of the adjacent property we made a B-line for the woods. The tall cedars and scrub oak made a fortress, and our destination was in the deepest, darkest part.

The air changed as soon as we entered the thick woody park. We scrambled down a shallow stream-bed and the sides grew taller and taller. After a few minutes jumping from rock to rock, and falling in the ankle-deep water twice, I looked up. We were standing under the slightly overhung face of a thirty-foot tall sandy wall. The Cliffs. These were our cliffs. We didn't own the land, but it seemed to us that no one had ever seen them. No one knew they were there. It was our place...our secret.

The only means of access and egress was a tiny trail leading up from the right. I led the way, with the other two following close behind. We were the only ones who knew where the trail was. I sank to my ankles in leaves and loose soil as I slogged my way closer to the caves near the top. Not natural caves. Caves we'd constructed over the last year or two. Every time we camped, we came back and dug them out more, making them wider, deeper, taller.

We made the top and all three of us squeezed into the largest opening. It was tight, and we decided it needed to be enlarged again. We only had a shovel and an old aluminum pot. One of us would have to use a stick.

The digging was good that day. The sandy soil was moist from recent rains and it scooped out of the hole like wet sugar. The closed canopy of the trees over the creek made it shady and somewhat dark, but it also kept the faint summer breeze from reaching us. We jumped in the shallow water of the creek to cool off, and then dug some more. When we'd finally had enough, and the creek wasn't sufficient, we took off for the nearby tank.

We wound along a faint path through the thick woods and each of us knew the way by heart. We all had on cutoffs, which doubled for swimsuits, so when we topped the bank we all just jumped in. I hit the surface and immediately lost all my breath. The icy water squeezed the air from my lungs. Even though it was summer, it was a natural spring-fed tank and the sun never seemed to have time to adequately warm the crystal-clear water. It was especially cold when I dangled my feet down toward the bottom. Exhilarating. A bit scary. But that didn't matter.

Words rolled excitedly from my mouth. It was great to be free in the woods with my friends. The warm sun melted the goose-bumps on my arms and shoulders as the last of the water rolled down my back and disappeared into thin air.

As we neared our campsite Simon and Lane walked side-by-side up the path, discussing something they'd done the weekend before. A twinge of jealousy worked its way into my thoughts.

They always have an inside joke or some fun secret.

I looked in from the edge, hoping to be part of the inside joke. Part of the secret.

I thought about…him. A momentary flash of our secret.

Had we been best friends?

Simon and Lane will probably get tired of me too.

Duke was following us, kind of behind and off to the side. I caught sight of him every now and then, weaving in and out, over and through the grass and brush. The lanky tan pup trotted through the woods, using his nose to rustle up any rabbits, birds, or large scaly fence lizards he might surprise. Just as we came to the back fence and were about to cross, we saw him running along the same path we'd taken on our way back to the cliffs before. It hit us all at the same time.

"Oh shit," we said together.

We jumped the fence as one and sprinted after him. He was at a full trot with his nose to the ground, zig zagging back and forth, on his way down the sandy creek bank. We called his name as we ran after him.

"Duke… Duke," we yelled.

We ran almost a half mile calling after him.

"Duke."

"Stop boy."

"Duke. Fucking get back here."

He didn't stop. We heard the metallic snap just as we reached the creek's viney brush-line. Duke let out a horrific yelp and began a rhythmic howling whine. He made the sound over and over.

Standing on top of the bank, we all stared down. Frozen. Afraid.

Simon's protective instincts kicked in and he started toward the bottom. Duke was just a tan wriggling blur as he pulled and yanked and tugged at the trap. The sounds he let out were like those I'd heard on Marty Stouffer's *Wild America*, when two wolves were fighting over food. I knew that if Simon ran down that bank and reached down to open the trap, Duke would surely attack. Fear shook me as I snatched at his shirt.

"Don't do it," I said. "He'll bite you."

"Let me go!" he yelled.

Simon pulled away and was just sliding down the bank, when it all stopped. The screeching whine still echoed through the creek bottom as we all looked at Duke and then each other.

"What happened?" Lane asked.

The dog's head hung low and foamy pink blood bubbled from his nose. A stream of thick maroon motor oil leaked from both corners of his mouth.

Simon slid the rest of the way down on his butt and started petting and hugging him. Duke whined, but it was only a normal, high-pitched dog sound. Not an attacking, growling wolf sound.

My eyes moved over to the trap. The two rusty, half-moon shaped metal sides must have sprung together with tremendous force. Duke's tongue was lying in the middle, next to the trip plate by the soggy bread. His thin tongue hadn't stood a chance. It was twitching and curling up on the end. It was perfect. And pink.

We walked single file toward the house. No one talked. Duke followed. He showed no ill effects from what had happened just moments earlier. The thin string of blood and bubbly saliva from his mouth swung in circles as it reached for the ground. Every now and then it would catch on one of the taller pieces of grass in the center of the trail and break off. A new string would immediately form.

As we quickened our pace, I thought about the twitching bubble gum colored tongue lying on the ground in the bottom of that creek.

Someone should go get it.

Maybe they can sew it back on.

Duke will be okay.

If they get him to the vet quickly enough…it would all be okay.

Why'd we set that fucking trap there anyway?

It wasn't okay.

They were only gone for an hour or so. As Simon and his mom drove back up the driveway toward the house, Lane and I jumped off of the porch and met their car at the turn. I looked in the dirty back window hoping to see Duke. Simon's tears and the dirt from his hands had stained his cheeks.

"Where's Duke?" I asked.

"He's dead," Simon answered.

And that was all. He didn't say anything else. His mom suggested that I come in and call my mom.

"You and Lane need to go home," she whispered.

The vet had said Duke was a goner, and that even if we'd rescued the tongue, he couldn't have saved him. Simon blamed me. He never said it, but I could tell.

I blamed me too. Duke was just an innocent pup. He had no idea. He was just eating a piece of bread that he thought someone had dropped on the ground. How could he have known it was a trap?

Why am I so stupid?

I held Simon back.

He could have released Duke's tongue before it ripped off.

If I wasn't such a chicken, Simon could have opened it and Duke would still be running around the pasture with us.

We would've still been camping. Looking at strange women in the Playboy. Telling jokes and laughing at each other's smelly farts. But we weren't doing any of those things.

Duke was dead.

Lane and I went home.

TWENTY

"Bradley Watson," the teacher called my name for the third time. I'd been staring at Tanya for at least fifteen minutes. She was my girlfriend. She'd said so. She was beautiful and she'd said she loved me. I think I loved her too. We never talked outside of class, just stared at each other in class. Staring was our thing. The excitement I felt when I was around her was unbearable. She made me feel cool. She scared me.

I tore my gaze from her and glanced up at the wonky-looking anatomy chart on the overhead projector. The bright orange bulb made the outlined female figure look sunburned.

"Bradley Watson. Are you here?" she asked.

"Present," I said.

I stared at the ground as Ms. Smith went through a litany of words and body parts I'd never heard of… or seen. Sweat began to moisten my palms.

Do they know what the hell she's talking about?

I didn't.

I'd heard some of the other guys talk about sex. They'd said they knew how to do it, but as Ms. Smith described the actual details of intercourse—the things that had to happen just to make it possible—I realized they'd been lying.

As she pointed to the boobs of the crude outlined woman on the wall, I felt a subtle excitement. My breath came heavier as I thought about what a girl might do to me. I was glad she didn't ask me to stand up.

Ms. Smith made a few jokes to lighten the mood. I looked around every time she said the word vagina, or penis, or erection. She also said words like testicle, vulva, clitoris, and ejaculate. I tried my best not to look embarrassed. When I met someone's gaze, I pasted on a smug little smile and acted as if I knew all of this stuff. Secretly I paid very close attention because I didn't know any of it.

Playboy had shown me the parts and pieces, but they didn't look much like what was on the wall. Excitement and fear competed for space in my mind. I wanted to have sex with Tanya. Or did I? The thought of her doing any of the things we'd just heard terrified me. How would I know what to do? Had she done it before?

I was staring at Tanya again, thinking that it may or may not be cool to have sex with her, when Ms. Smith said the words, "sexual abuse." I was only half-listening since I already knew about the boogey men in white vans. Kidnappers. Basements. Dark closets. Same old boring stuff.

But then everything stopped as her words came out stilted and in slow motion. "Neighbor."

"Older."

"Intimate."

"Touching."

"Age."

"S..E..X..U..A..L   A..B..U..S..E."

"Inappropriate."

"G..A..M..E..S."

And then, "T..E..L..L.. S..O..M..E..O..N..E."

It didn't register at first. I played back what I'd just heard.

I felt a hot boulder in the pit of my stomach and my mouth felt as if it were full of cotton balls. My pulse swished loudly in my ears. My chest was pounding. I reflexively stood up and found the door. I didn't ask. I bolted. I slid around the corner, past Mr. Sanderson's office and down the hall to the bathroom. I stared in the mirror. I stared at my confusion. I saw my anger. I was repulsed by my image.

What the hell?

What the fuck?

I punched the mirror and immediately threw up in the sink.

I didn't go back to class. I couldn't. I made a B-line for the front door, walked outside, stepped off the short curb, and crossed the narrow gravelly street. I felt another punch in my guts and threw up in the ditch on

the other side. The four-block walk to my house took an hour. I couldn't
see anything around me. I was in a tunnel – a blurry grey tunnel. No trees.
No cars. No houses. No birds, insects, dogs, cats, kids, bikes, grass,
lawnmowers, sprinklers. Nothing.

I was walking home, but not directly. I subconsciously went the
long way, avoiding his house. Avoiding him. I thought back to all those
times. So vivid. They all came at me. The room – fish, aquarium, hunting,
skinning. The chicken coop. The car. The farm. The couch. The deer camp.
My house. His house. The river. Everywhere. I ducked into the alley and
threw up again.

It wasn't a game. It had never been a game.

It was SEX.

I was twelve now. He was twenty…no, twenty-one…or twenty-
two. He was grown. Maybe he hadn't stopped coming around because I'd
made him mad.

Was it all my fault?

Did I do something to make him want to have sex with me?

Did I really have sex with him?

Was it sex if I didn't know it was sex?

It was…It was.

I stumbled up the steps and into my room. I didn't bother taking
my shoes off and didn't hear Mom when she said, "don't slam the door." I
went to the closet, slumped down on the floor, and grabbed the old brown
boot. They'd been my favorites for a year, but I never wore them anymore.

I just sat there. Visions of him. Visions of all those times. All those
places. I turned up the left boot and waited for the thin curl of silver metal
to fall into my palm. I'd made it one day on impulse and had used it often.
It had once been a paperclip, but was now a tool, used only when needed.

It was needed now.

I slid the paperclip into my pocket and walked out the back door. I
was still in a trance. Confused. The thoughts just kept involuntarily swirling
around my head.

What did I do?

Did I make it happen?

Did I like it?

The Johnson grass behind the back yard was tall. It touched my
fingertips as I headed for the river. The grass laid over as my footsteps

came down. I probably should have already mown it. I blindly walked down the narrow rocky trail toward the murky green water. Rain had recently washed away some of the dirt and exposed large red rocks, most of the way down. My foot rolled off the side of a loose round one and I barely caught myself on some vines. I found my balance, and some sketchy footing, while slipping and sliding my way to the bottom.

I arrived at my spot. My favorite spot. I walked across the steel grates of the dock and sat down on the end. I took off my high-tops and chunked them over on the dirt path, about half way up the bank. The heels of my feet barely touched the surface as they dangled freely and swung back and forth. The water wasn't exactly muddy, but it had a creamy green feel. A leaf swirled and circled in the eddy beside the dock, touching the sucking funnel in the middle, then bouncing out to the edge, time and again.

It was quiet. No frogs. No birds. No people. Just me, and the realization of what had happened to me. He hadn't really liked me. He hadn't liked hanging out with me or playing all those stupid games. I wasn't special. He only wanted to have sex with me. And, I was a boy.

I'd sharpened the point of that paper clip many times. I had a wet stone for sharpening my hunting knife and it worked just as well on the tiny silver tip. I'd honed it down to needle sharp. It glistened and I felt the bees beginning to flit around in my stomach. My heart sped up and I felt the anticipation of what was to come…of what always came.

Careful.

I didn't want to drop it in the river.

I poked my arm, just above the barely healed scratch. I poked below, and then to each side. It was my ritual.

Top.

Bottom.

Left.

Right.

I started toward the back and worked forward. Always the same. Tiny scratches at first, just to break the skin. As I scratched my heart slowed. My breathing became calm and even. A little deeper. Deeper. And…blood. I didn't stop until I saw blood. I never stopped until I saw blood.

It hurt a little. It felt good. The sensation numbed my mind and took away the throbbing pain I'd felt in my chest and gut just seconds before. As I focused on the thin red line, and the drops of blood pooling at both ends, no thoughts entered my mind. I didn't think about him or what he did to me…or what I'd done. I didn't think about what people would say when they found out. No one could ever find out. From the first poke, the thoughts stopped. I was present. I was here. I was back in control.

The next morning came too quickly. I didn't want to go back. I didn't want to face my friends.

"I have a stomach ache," I lied.

It worked. I laid in my room and stared out the long window for hours. The familiar oak outside was tall and steady. Its arching limbs barely moved as the breeze blew down the gravel driveway and rustled the leaves. I was hungry. I hadn't eaten the early breakfast Mom had fixed. That was one downfall of using the stomachache excuse. Mom was gone and Dad was out, so I made my way into the kitchen, grabbed some chips and took them to my room.

I ate the salty snacks three or four at a time, shoving them into my mouth and wiping greasy crumbs on my bedspread. The birds held my attention. Whenever I skipped school, I watched them all day. They were always there. Mourning Doves, Inca Doves, Carolina Chickadees, Northern Cardinals, Blue Jays, and two or three kinds of sparrows. They flew into the oak, over to the rickety fence-line with the long-gone honeysuckle blooms, down to the shrubs, and into the gravel below my window. They pecked at the reddish rocky dirt that Dad had brought in for the road. They chased grasshoppers and beetles. They chased each other. I knew they would be there and I counted on them.

I'd shot at them and chased them around the woods by the river. But when I needed them…they were there. So, I just watched. I watched them until the day slipped away and they left my window view and headed for some far away night roost.

After two days of lying in bed, Mom suggested that it was time for me to head back to school. I didn't want to go back. I especially didn't want to go back to Ms. Smith's class. I couldn't hear those words again. I didn't want to think about those words again. I didn't want to think about him again. Ever.

I decided never to tell anyone.

Ms. Smith had said we should tell if we'd ever known anyone who was sexually abused. I knew better. I couldn't tell her. I couldn't tell Mr. Sanderson. I couldn't tell my friends. And I couldn't tell Mom and Dad. They'd all know it was my fault. I hadn't said no.

I should have said no.

I was numb.

Eventually, I went back to school. I played football and basketball. I ran track. I ran the 300-meter low hurdles. Coach Hart said that even though I was short and white, I had the best form he'd seen in a long time. I never won a race.

I broke up with Tanya. I broke up with everyone. I felt dirty. Deep down I knew that they all knew. Maybe they didn't know exactly what had happened, but they all knew I was different. I knew they all talked about me when I wasn't around.

TWENTY-ONE

I showed up to the party early and milled around with the others near the end of the long narrow driveway. It was Jamie's birthday and we were all excited about the hayride. I stealthily looked around to see if I could spot her long shiny black hair. It didn't matter much. She had no idea I liked her anyway.

My eyes took a few seconds to refocus as I stopped looking for her and stared up at the white moon. A slight breeze brought just enough chill to raise goose bumps on my arm.

I had on my favorite maroon jacket and suddenly noticed the tiny rip in the sleeve, just above the cuff. I reached down and plucked out the exposed white, fluffy down feather, and the rip was once again invisible. We all bunched up near the trailers.

Hay-bales had been stacked around the edges of the big flat trailers and loose hay was piled in the center. We could either sit on the bench that was created by the bales around the edge, or in the loose hay in the middle.

I climbed up and sat in an empty spot near the rear edge of the last trailer. My feet swung back and forth through the air and I wondered who would sit next to me. I was nervous. Everyone had coupled up, and like most of these parties, it would be a huge make-out session before we ever started rolling. I'd heard my friends talking on the playground about how to unhook bras and unbutton pants. They'd also talked about how to know when your hand was down the pants just far enough. I had no idea. I didn't plan on getting with anyone because I didn't think anyone wanted to get with me. And if I did end up with someone, I wouldn't know what to do anyway.

We took off with a jerk and the hay bale I sat on rocked backwards. I leaned in the opposite direction and kept it, and me, from tumbling off the back of the squatty trailer. We sped down the road as hay swirled around, up, and all over us. After the caravan had gone a mile or two down the road, she suddenly jumped over the edge and plopped down next to me. It was her. She was wearing her signature long black shiny Pocahontas braids.

Oh shit…Summer.

My bowels felt slack. I worried that my insides would all come out at once. I wanted her so bad.

Thoughts of Ms. Smith's class flickered through my head. It had been a year since that crazy day. Intermingled thoughts of boobs, vaginas, kissing, foreplay, and sex swirled around. I tried to remember how Ms. Smith had said it all worked. I tried not to think about the last part of that class.

Should I talk?

Should I touch her?

My jaw felt wired shut. I couldn't turn thoughts into words. They wouldn't move past my lips.

Summer had moved to town a couple of years before seventh grade. Her almond-shaped brown eyes and freckles had won me over instantly. I'd secretly longed for her since the first time I saw her. No matter who I was "dating" at the time, I loved Summer. Always Summer. I sat as close to her as I could get at every assembly. I knew which part of the lunchroom she ate in, and who she hung out with after school. She never paid attention to me and I never told anyone about my feelings. I daydreamed about walking down by the river with her. We always held hands and talked about frogs and fishing and bikes. She always wanted to stop at the dock and look out across the wide, easy flowing water. She'd turn to me and come in for a kiss…

I'd never gotten past that scene. I never thought it would happen. And now…here she was…staring at me. She blinked her brown eyes. Her long curved lashes fluttered like soft butterfly wings.

I thought about jumping off the back, right there in the middle of the road, and letting that trailer just disappear into the darkness. I'd imagined this moment so many times.

Here it is.

Here she is.

I didn't jump. I stared back, still struggling for words. Finally, I asked if she was cold and gave her my jacket. I hoped she didn't notice the rip in the sleeve.

She put it on.

"Are you gonna kiss me?" she asked.

I did.

We didn't come up for breath the entire ride. I kissed her desperately with my open mouth and finally figured out what she kept doing with her tongue. The first time she stuck it in my mouth I just stuck mine back in hers and wiggled it around. I finally got the hang of her clockwise circular pattern, and it seemed easy after that.

I kissed her. She kissed me.

She was lying on the stiff bed of straw and looking up at me. Wind and hay swirled around us as the trucks and trailers sped down the road. The moon made her skin appear snow white and her freckles looked like cinnamon dashed across vanilla ice cream.

Others were kissing all around us. The entire trailer looked like a pit of eighth grade snakes writhing around on top of each other and flicking their forked tongues in and out and all around. I looked over at a buddy and noticed his hand under his girl's shirt. It was on her boob and he was moving it round and round. He kept squeezing and squeezing. It reminded me of Grandma kneading dough to make homemade bread.

This was it. I tried to will my right hand to move. I imagined it sliding inside the jacket, under her blue t-shirt, under her tight-fitting bra. I was mortified…it wouldn't move. The hay underneath us suddenly felt like needles sticking into my arm. I heard Queen singing "Another One Bites the Dust" on the boom-box in the background.

I came up for another breath and noticed her gleaming white teeth smiling at me. Was she smiling because she was having fun or laughing inside at the stupid way I kissed? Maybe she was smiling and asking me to please slide my hand under her shirt and knead her huge boobs like all the other guys on the trailer. She kept smiling. My heartbeat kept swishing in my ears.

I thought about jumping off the trailer again. This time I'd run into the woods. I thought about pretending I was sick and walking back to the house. I thought about sliding my hand under that shirt.

I had to do it. I had to. She grabbed my head and pulled me down to kiss some more. I reached up and touched her thick, shiny hair. I touched her shoulder. I moved my hand down slowly but couldn't make it stop where I wanted it to stop. It missed the boob and ended up at the bottom of her shirt. I felt her skin, right where the jeans stopped and the shirt began. I inched it upward, trying not to be too conspicuous, and froze again when I touched her belly button. My index finger circled it.

Am I supposed to touch that?

She kept kissing me. Her tongue and my mind both swirled. My hand continued upward, barely touching her silky skin.

Upward.

I should probably stop.

Upward.

She'll probably punch me if I touch it.

Upward.

Bra!

I touched the bottom seam of the silky bra and immediately eased my hand back out from under her shirt. I tucked it under her leg and stopped kissing her. I had to breathe. I held my head up and looked at her again. She was still smiling. My stomach churned and I felt like I might throw up on her. She wanted to kiss some more but I had to wait. I didn't want to throw up in her mouth.

After a minute or two, we kissed again. My hand refused to venture back under the shirt and that's as far as I got. I had touched her bra. I didn't touch what was under it, but I had at least been close. It was as far as I'd ever been. She seemed to enjoy the kissing and I felt I was pretty great at it by the time the trailers pulled back around to the starting point.

We jumped down from the rear row of bales and she handed me my jacket. I put it on. It smelled like her perfume. Sweet. Spicy. Soft. I swirled my foot around in the gravel, pushing a small black rock back and forth and around in circles.

She smiled and disappeared into the darkness. I eased around inside the circling crowd of people. My chest was out and my head was high.

Summer.

It had really happened. All those thoughts. All those fantasies and scenarios. They hadn't even been close. It was so much better. Her eyes. Her lips. Her skin. So much better.

Diana Ross sang "Endless Love" as I walked toward Mom's car.

TWENTY-TWO

It was Monday, but the fact it was a school day didn't bother me much. I had ventured into new territory over the weekend and I knew that some of the guys had seen me mugging down with Summer. I knew they'd ask questions and I'd be ready with answers. I had mugged down with the girl I'd secretly been in love with for almost four years.

The day went by slowly. I had to be strategic. I didn't have Summer in class and that was the best part of my day. I really wanted to see her, to kiss her again. But those thoughts brought on an immediate panic.

I knew I'd never be able to talk to her again. What would I say? There was nothing to talk about except Saturday night, and I surely couldn't talk about that. It had been great. Maybe the best night of my life. It had made me feel normal. I was terrified of even seeing her in the hall.

I walked out of the bathroom and slowed near the corner. Inching steadily forward, I peered around the edge. The coast was clear. I bounced into the flow of other kids and headed for my next class. I knew her schedule and which classes she had so I avoided them. In fact, I avoided that side of the building completely.

The guys were hanging out in front of the lockers when I walked into the gym. We had to suit up for football practice and I was thinking about how my undershirt had smelled like dead crickets the week before. Coach only washed them once every couple of weeks. Mine was awful.

The small mob suddenly got quiet as I walked up. One of my buddies stepped to the side.

"How was Summer?" he asked.

"What do you mean?"

"How did she kiss?" he asked.

"Great." I said with a too-big smile.

"Are her boobs as big as they look in that sweater she has on today?" he asked.

I looked down. I went back to the kissing. I had to focus on the kissing.

"She's a great kisser," I said.

"How about those boobs?" he demanded.

"I'm not sure about the boobs."

"What do you mean?" another one of them asked. "Why?"

"I only got to the bra," I said.

I'd kissed Summer all night...Summer. I'd touched her bra...her bra. Summer's bra. I thought that would surely impress them.

It did not.

One of the bunch said he'd seen my hand under her shirt and thought that I'd for sure gotten to second base. I told him I'd touched the bra, so in essence, I'd touched second base. He said that didn't count...no boob, no second base. His brother, a year younger but taller, stepped forward and said he'd talked to Summer that morning. She'd had a lot to say about me.

I smiled. I'd kissed her long and kissed her hard. I knew it would be good.

It was not.

"Your breath was bad," he said. "She didn't like the taste of your mouth."

"What?" I almost choked.

"You had too much spit in your mouth when you kissed," he laughed. "She said your teeth were green and you don't know how to kiss."

He looked at his brother and the rest of the gang. All the air left my lungs at once. I looked at the floor, trying to think of something to say. There was nothing.

They all laughed, directly in my face.

I put my stinky football clothes back on the little rusty hook and dropped my cleats in the bottom of the locker. Last week's dried mud crumbled off and created a small puff of dust. I walked out and went straight home.

I walked in the front door, and went straight to my closet, straight for the boot, straight for my paperclip. I walked out of the house, across the yard, down the path and along the bank. I sat on the dock and went over the words I'd just heard, once, twice, three times.

My breath was bad.

My teeth were green.

I pretty much slobbered on her.

She thinks I'm a bad kisser and probably thinks something's wrong with me because I didn't slide my hand under her bra.

Any normal guy would have touched her boob.

I wanted to.

She didn't stop me.

She wanted me to.

What's wrong with me?

Something's definitely wrong with me.

I touched the point to my skin. Above. Then, below. Left. Right.

I did it again, but harder this time. And, again. Above, below, left, right.

Harder.

I jammed it in.

I was already bleeding. It didn't hurt. I wouldn't let it hurt. I pushed the little sharp edge in and raked it across my arm. It was fast and careless. I missed the usual scratch and watched a thin, clean gash open up just below. It was deeper than usual and I thought for a second that I might need to tell Mom. It might've needed a stitch or two. It bled. The clip was sharp. I kept it that way. The cut was clean and deep, but when I pinched my fingers together on both sides, it stopped bleeding.

No, I wouldn't tell Mom. I wouldn't tell anyone. It was my secret. I was good at secrets. My breathing slowed.

Their words stopped.

Her words stopped.

I walked around school with my head low. Everyone was laughing at me and I was sure she'd told everyone by now about my breath and green teeth and slobber. I had a hard time concentrating on Algebra, History, Literature or Computer Science. I could only think about how much my armpits were sweating. I worried people would notice them running down the sides of my shirt. The bees in my stomach sped up to a tornado swirl when any teacher asked any student to stand and recite answers or write on the board. All the while, I worried I'd be next.

I imagined what they thought. Me doing things I shouldn't have with him. Summer grabbing my hand and pulling it toward her naked boob. Me pulling my hand away, repulsed by her. Repulsed by her naked skin. I knew they knew something was wrong with me.

How can they not know?

TWENTY-THREE

Christmas morning had come and gone. I hadn't asked for much. And the one thing I'd wanted, the REO Speedwagon – *High Infidelity* cassette tape, had somehow been mixed up. I'd gotten REO Speewagon all right. But, it was a tape I'd never heard of – *You Can Tune a Piano But You Can't Tuna Fish*.

What the hell?

I was glad to be back at Simon's and glad to have a smile back on my face. I'd been angry with Mom and Dad for the rest of the morning, fake smiling my way through the rest of my presents. The anger still simmered below the surface and I hadn't hidden it very well. I'd played a few games with Luke and Josh. My parents asked me questions, cajoling me, knowing I was upset. I answered. Short answers. Snotty answers. Then, I'd sat in my room with my new Lite Brite and created some colorful circles and an eye. A fucking Lite Brite!

Simon and I were going to camp that night. His mom said it was too cold, but we knew our fire would be huge and we'd be warm enough. Besides, Simon said he had something else that would keep us warm. He didn't give any hints, and I had no idea what the hell he was talking about. I imagined a battery powered electric blanket or some kind of battery powered socks.

I hadn't stayed at his house since the Duke incident. He never mentioned it after the day it happened. He'd seen me at the corner store a few days after and acted as if nothing had happened. That was okay with me. I still blamed myself. I was glad he didn't.

He showed me his presents, and I didn't mention the cassette tape fiasco. I had brought the tape and was going to give it to him later. He had a cassette deck in the house and I thought it would make a great gift…just not for me. He seemed happy about his presents and all the great food they'd eaten a few hours before. It was warm in the house, but I was ready to head for the woods. The woods created a special kind of excitement inside me. The trees. The tent. The fire. The grown-upness of it all. No parents. No rules.

We slipped sideways through the little gate and squished through the shitty mud, back across the pens. A couple of skinny, black and white spotted calves bucked around us and tried to follow us through the fence when we reached the other side. We ducked under the limb at our usual fence crossing and went straight for our usual campsite. I carried the little yellow pop up tent under my arm and Simon had two large paper bags full of camping necessities. The bags were both stuffed, but I could only see bread, chocolate, marshmallows, and matches in the one closest to me. I figured the toilet paper was in there somewhere.

With the tent set up, and wood stacked in a large teepee shape in the middle of our pit, we built the fire.

Simon liked to use tons of gasoline. Sometimes we used diesel, which burned slower and was much safer. But Simon liked the excitement of dumping half of a five-gallon can on the pile, creating a thin trail to a somewhat safe standing spot, and dropping his match.

This time was no exception. He dumped the entire contents of the gas can, which was at least half full, made a trail about ten feet long and stopped.

"You're not far enough away," I said.

He assured me that he was.

I scooted back another few feet and watched him strike the match. He scraped two of the blue-tipped, strike anywhere matches against their bright blue box. They blazed up and he waited, just a couple of seconds before dropping them. He dropped both matches simultaneously…

WHHHHUUUUMMMPPPPP.

I felt the shockwave hit my chest. By the time he'd made the little trail and lit the match and stood there for fifteen seconds, the gasoline vapor had silently and invisibly made its way out to where Simon was standing. When the vapor ring ignited, a ten-foot wide ball of explosive fire shot upwards and outwards. Simon was standing within its reach. I had luckily moved just outside the circle.

He jumped around like a grasshopper on hot pavement. The legs of his jeans and the right arm of his coat were blazing orange and yellow, and he howled as he jumped.

I was frozen in place. My feet wouldn't move. I didn't know what to do.

He kept jumping and running.

Finally, I remembered.

"Stop, drop and roll," I yelled to him.

He howled and ran more.

I ran over and tackled him in the crispy leaves and grass. The flames jumped off him and onto the dry litter. We looked at each other and started kicking and scraping at the burning ground. We noticed more orange and yellow blaze to our left. The tent was on fire.

I jumped off Simon and ran over to the tent. It wasn't really on fire. The bush next to it had a bit of flame, but the tent only had some dime-sized melted holes in the top and front flap.

Simon was back up and looked no worse for the wear. The left sleeve of his coat was peppered with tiny melted spots, but other than that, he wasn't burned.

We surveyed the black grass and charred leaves. Our eyes both went to the fire pit at the same time. We were cold. We needed more wood…and a new fire.

Dark came down and we sat on opposite sides of the newly refurbished blaze. We'd re-stacked most of the logs from our earlier attempt, smaller stuff on the bottom, and applied the remaining few drops of gasoline from the can. Yellow and pink flames curled around the cedar limbs and coals were just forming underneath the pile. They twinkled like city lights from an airplane when the slight north wind fanned them with its icy breath. Stars were bright and I traced the only constellation I knew, the big dipper, with my finger. We were settling down for a cold night.

Simon went over to the tent and unzipped the tightly pulled flap that created the front door. He ducked inside for a minute or two and came out with something in his hand. He held it behind his back and smiled. It was the same smile he'd smiled at church, the day we ate and drank Christ.

He slowly brought his hands around and I could just make out a clear flat bottle with a black label. He unscrewed the cap, put it to his lips and took a sip. A small sip. I expected a couple of glugs like the Christ wine, but this sip only produced one small amber bubble.

"Yeeeoooowwwww," he screeched when he was done.

He handed the bottle to me. After the screeching yeow, I wasn't too sure I wanted any part of it.

I took the bottle in my hands and read the label. Jack Daniels Old No. 7 Tennessee Sour Mash Whiskey. I remembered sipping whiskey from my cousin's cup at the New Year's party a couple years before. It wasn't good. I put the bottle to my lips and hesitated.

Simon looked at me with a smile that implied I might be chicken.

I assured him I was not by turning it up and taking three gulps. Three bubbles rolled their way up through the amber liquid. I looked at Simon. I turned around immediately…and threw up.

Luckily, we had some Cokes with us and he said it was best mixed with something else. Ah, Coke. I'd learned that trick from Paw Paw. He always mixed his with an icy cold Coke. My cousin had used Dr. Pepper. It had been bad. I wondered if the Coke would make it taste better. We weren't drinking Old Crow, but I was sure I only needed a little of the Jack Daniels to make an appropriate mixture. Or at least one I could stomach. We each drank a couple of sips from our Coke cans and added a little Jack. I only added two bubbles worth. It didn't quite fill up the can, but after tasting and throwing up the earlier amount, two bubbles seemed like it would be enough.

Simon did the same and we settled down by the fire and sipped our cans. I gave him the REO Speedwagon tape and we decided to listen to it right then. Simon pressed play on our little camping radio. The cassette player clicked loudly as we both realized the tape was in backwards and needed to be turned over. We tried singing along, but neither of us had ever heard most of those songs. So, we mostly laughed. We laughed when "The Unidentified Flying Tuna Trot" finally came on. What the hell kind of song title was that anyway? But it was an instrumental, and after a few more sips, it sounded pretty damn good. We replayed it about a hundred times. I felt a tinge of regret for giving him the tape.

The sweet taste from my Coke can coated my throat and the volatile vapor drifted up through my sinuses. I tasted it but seemed to smell it even more as I drank. It was so warm going down and my throat started feeling tingly and numb. Simon was laughing at the black soot on his pant legs from our earlier fire fiasco. I laughed too and before we knew it we couldn't stop. We laughed and laughed. My head was feeling a little dizzy and I asked for another pour of whiskey – it had only taken a few sips and Jack and I were on a first name basis.

I noticed a calm warm energy was radiating from my stomach not unlike the calm feeling I had when I used my paperclip. My words came easily too, and I didn't second guess them. Even my laughter came easy. Everything seemed funny and light.

I refilled the few drinks I'd taken from the can. More whiskey, less Coke. It tasted pretty much the same, so I continued sipping. Simon was refilling as well, and we'd drank about a quarter of the bottle. The fire felt good and the Jack and Coke was starting to taste pretty great.

I finished the whole Coke and went over by the tent and grabbed another one. This time I just poured half of it on the ground and refilled the empty part of the can with Jack. Simon did the same and the bottle only seemed to have a little left in the bottom. It was less than a quarter full.

We laughed and drooled over a Hustler magazine he'd ripped off from his brother. I'd never seen boobs so big. They didn't look normal. As I stared at those giant breasts, I felt my crotch get kind of numb and tingly. I wanted to reach into that page and grab her. As I stared at that woman, I made a promise to myself. Next time I had the opportunity, I wouldn't hesitate to grab one. I'd grab it and knead it like dough, just like Grandma did with the bread, and just like the other guys on that hayride had. As the warmth continued to flow from my stomach down to my crotch, I felt confident. I knew I'd do it. I knew I wouldn't chicken out next time.

I felt my bladder filling, expanding like a water balloon. I had to pee. I stood up at my normal standing up speed, and quickly sat back down. I tried again, and managed to stay upright, but a little wobbly.

What the hell?

I'd felt myself getting warm, and happy. I'd noticed Simon talking a little differently, kind of slurry. But I didn't expect to be wobbly when I tried to go pee. I took a step, then another. I made it to the usual pee bush – a short gnarly cedar growing low by the fence. I peed. Then had to pee a little more. Then, one more squirt.

I looked up from zipping and noticed Simon peeing on the fire. I laughed and yelled at him to stop it. It stunk like the concentrated pee smell from those long urinal troughs at the American Legion. He laughed and kept peeing.

"Watch this," he said. "Watch my pee."

He pointed and kept peeing. The stream of pee turned to pee-steam when it hit the coals.

"I see it," I laughed.

"No but look. It turns to steam," he laughed.

"I see it," I said. I tried to stop laughing so I could talk.

"Look, I'm still peeing," he said. He was peeing and laughing and wobbling.

"I see it," I said again. "Now fucking stop it. The whole camp smells like piss."

I sat back down, kind of. Rather, I sat on the front edge of my partially-rusted metal folding chair, and it tipped. I landed on my right side, smack dab in the middle of the fire. I jumped like a scared cat and rolled toward Simon. Luckily, I didn't have flames coming off my body like he had earlier. But I did smell something.

My right sideburn had melted a bit. It wasn't really even a sideburn, just some hair that the barber had left there to look like one. The normal length sideburn hairs created a contrast for the newly burned and shriveled pubic looking hairs all around them. My eyebrow was singed as well, and my nose was filled with a pungent burning smell. Simon couldn't stop laughing. I wasn't burned, so I laughed too.

We were best friends. I felt it. All the worry that Simon might be better friends with someone else or that he didn't really like me, were further washed away with each drink. It was a new feeling. Confident.

Then I walked back to the pee tree…and threw up on it.

The next morning…I woke with a start…and threw up. Hammers pounded the inside of my skull. My stomach flipped and twirled like pizza dough flying through the air. I couldn't swallow. I stood up and sat back down immediately. Simon was still laying in his sleeping bag. It was almost noon.

How did we sleep so late?

We always seemed to get up at daybreak with the noise from birds and other critters.

I knew immediately that I'd lost something. The ease and confidence were gone. Completely gone. It was just me again. I started to sweat as guilt made its way in and took over with its little nagging voice.

Why did I drink?

Why did we look at naked girls?

Simon probably didn't think I was funny.

He probably isn't really my best friend.

I looked at the grey ashy fire-pit and thought about lighting it up again. We always lit the fire first thing in the morning and had white bread toast and mustard. It didn't taste great, but it had become a tradition. On a past trip, we'd run out of jelly and every other condiment except mustard. So, we ate mustard toast that morning and every camping morning since. I thought about mustard toast...and threw up.

Simon and I got drunk a few more times that year. It was like a roller coaster. When we were camping and drinking, I felt invincible. When we weren't, I didn't.

Mostly, eighth grade just blurred by. After the guys stopped ragging me about Summer, I fell into a quiet, numb routine. I avoided Summer at all costs, and most other girls, too. I didn't know what to believe. Was I a bad kisser? Did the guys make that shit up? I didn't know.

I did know that alcohol made me feel good. Really good.

TWENTY-FOUR

Matt showed up a few minutes early to pick me up. He was my favorite
cousin, and he lived down the street with my aunt—the same aunt who'd
conspired with Mom to hide our Christmas presents. I'd started my first
real job a few weeks before freshman year. Another Aunt and Uncle owned
the local food locker, and I worked there when I wasn't in school –
summers and weekends.

Weekends were the best because Matt always picked me up in his
monster truck. Chevy Silverado. Two-tone grey paint. Huge lift kit. The
tires stood waist high and said *Gumbo Monster Mudder* on the outsides. It
was so tall I couldn't look in the back without climbing up on the bumper.
The stereo system was loud. Really loud. We proved it every Saturday
morning before work...cruising the Y with the windows down.

I opened the door, grabbed the grey cloth seat with my left hand
and the hard elbow rest on the door with my right. I'd perfected my jump
slide after a few weeks. I rocked back as far as I could and made the two-
stepped jump and ended up right in my usual spot.

"Got your lunch?"

I jumped back down, bounded up the porch and slammed the
screen door as I headed for the kitchen. Mom stood there with a smile,
holding my lunch bag in front of her.

"Don't slam the door." I barely heard her as I jumped back up into
my spot in the big truck.

"Let's roll," I said. I looked at Matt as if I'd been waiting on him
the whole time.

Van Halen had just put out *1984*, even though it was still 1983. Matt pushed in the new tape. The Pioneer cassette deck clicked as it engaged. We didn't move until the first song began. Eddie started us off with that eerie cool intro and they went right into "Jump." It sounded so good cranking through that Punch amp and those four six-by-nine speakers he had behind the seat. We only made it through "Panama" before ending up in the parking lot at work. I couldn't wait for the end of the day, and the rest of that tape.

We did no butchering or sausage making that Saturday. The first customer came in, told us his name, and Matt looked up the order number. I was already pulling on the old worn-out fireman's coat. I waited for him to give me the number, then I pulled the handle and cracked open the big aluminum door. It had accumulated ice around the cracks overnight and I broke some off with the hammer we left in the corner.

I finally got the door open, stepped inside, and slammed it hard behind me.

That smell. Frozen. Ice. Cold. I could never put a better description to it. Just the smell of the freezer. It always scared me a little.

What if I can't get back out?

What if the power goes off and I get lost behind the isles of frozen meat?

The temperature in the freezer hovered between twenty-eight and thirty-two degrees Fahrenheit. Frigid.

Small orders were easy and I never felt too cold. Larger orders like that one kept me inside the frosty box much longer. The cold started seeping into my body after about five minutes. I didn't let on though. I'd gotten a reputation for being able to stay in there and get the job done. Some of the other workers had to come out and take a break every few minutes, but not me. It felt good to be recognized for something. I made sure I did everything at work to the best of my ability. I liked the attention I got for doing a good job.

The blocks of frozen meat clunked together as I transferred them from the freezer shelf to the wire basket. The basket fit perfectly inside two rails on an old metal cart. When the basket was full I hauled ass toward the entrance.

Boom.

The cart hit the door full speed and it slammed open and banged against the outside wall. Matt was used to the abrupt noise and didn't look up. The customer stared wide-eyed as the loaded cart pulled me into the front room. My rubber boots slid across the slick floor as I did my best to get it stopped.

We stacked the frozen blocks of meat inside big brown paper sacks as best we could. When they were near overflowing, we crumpled the tops down and humped them out to the customers' truck.

Busy work. Easy work. The morning sped by.

"You want to go out and feed corn at the ranch after work?" Matt asked near the end of our shift.

Deer season was only a couple months away and he was getting them accustomed to being near his hunting blinds.

"Fucking A." I loved hunting, and I also loved that monster truck. And I couldn't wait until next weekend to hear the rest of that Van Halen tape.

We locked up and grabbed a couple of sandwiches from Zane's BBQ next door on our way out. It was the best BBQ in town and was owned by the same Uncle that owned the food locker. The sandwiches were made from leftover chopped beef. They were also free.

We threw the bag on the seat and both did our rocking jumps up into the truck. Matt cranked the stereo and Van Halen played "Top Jimmy". We were off. Windows down, music up, flying down the highway in that big-ass truck.

I jumped out to open the gate.

"Grab me a beer out of the back," he said. "And get one for you too."

I hesitated.

Did I hear him right?

I jumped up and grabbed the top of the tailgate. I pushed off the bumper and bounded over the edge. I reached in and swirled my hand down between all the small clear cubes and grabbed at two of the bronze round shaped tops. They were the only thing visible beneath the ice. I grabbed two cans and pulled them out, handed them in through the sliding back window. The lid squawked as I closed the little red Igloo cooler and jumped to the ground...all in one fluid motion.

After leaping back in the truck, I held my beer. Held it. Looked at it.

I'd drank with Simon and snuck a couple beers from Dad's cooler at fish fries and cookouts. This felt different. It was the first time someone who was old enough to drink had actually asked me if I wanted a beer. I continued to stare at the bright white can. It had half melted ice cubes stuck to the top rim and some were sliding down the sides. The frosty condensation gave the red oval in the middle a soft pinkish look and I could barely read the words – *A Fine Pilsner Beer.*

"You gonna look at it, or fucking drink it?" Matt asked.

I popped the tab, peeled off the teardrop shaped top, and tossed it on the floor. I put it to my lips and took a small sip. Bitter. But it was ice cold. After a couple more sips, it went down smoothly. It was really fizzy and I kept burping. Matt always cracked his window when he burped.

"Smells like a mouth fart."

I started doing the same. I finished the beer, crunched the middle of the can and tossed it through the open slider. I figured I was lucky to have had a beer with my cousin and felt kind of like a grown up.

"You want another one?" he asked.

"Hell yeah," I said.

The wooded lane was narrow. The giant truck barely squeezed by some of the huge elder and oak limbs. We jumped down and began slinging corn all around us.

"I've seen a lot of deer in this spot," he said.

Deer sign was everywhere. Hoof prints and poop were visible across the whole field. I dipped the large plastic cup into the fifty-pound bag of yellowish-orange kernels. Corn dribbled over the lip as I pulled it out. Reaching as far as I could behind my back, I made a huge sideways arc with my arm as my body twisted in a full circle. I must have looked like I was throwing the discus at a track meet. The corn rattled out of the hollow cup as it dispersed, flew through the air, and hailed down in the green grass all around us. I repeated the motion again and again.

"That should be enough," Matt said.

We moved to another spot and did the same thing.

After dumping the last of the corn from the last of the bags, we grabbed another cold one and made our way back out to the main highway. I closed the gate and jumped back in. He stepped on the gas. With the windows down, the roaring sound of those big mud grip tires on the highway almost drowned out the stereo. We passed the Smithville city limit sign on our way in, made the Y a couple of times, and Matt said he needed to get home. KISS was singing "Lick It Up" as I finished my fifth beer and the big-ass truck turned up our street.

I felt warm. Confident. Happy.

TWENTY-FIVE

Light. My eyes were closed but it still seemed bright. I cracked my right eye to see what the hell was going on. Dusty sunlight was shining through a crack in the center of some drab curtains. Just a tiny slit. Just enough for the beam to find its way to my throbbing dry eye.

What the hell?

I looked up and noticed the cracked popcorn stucco on the ceiling.

Where am I?

And who the hell is under the covers next to me?

I tried to remember.

How did I get here?

Where the hell is here?

Thinking made my head throb. Snippets of memory came back. Drinking some beers with Matt. I'd drank a lot of beers with Matt in the few months since I'd started working down at the food locker. I enjoyed our talks about music, girls, and town drama.

Yesterday. We'd gotten off work, road the Y a few times, drank six or eight beers, and then he'd dropped me off. I'd taken a shower and gone out with a couple of buddies. I'd ridden around in the back seat of the maroon Chevelle while Dire Straits sang about "Money for Nothing" and told me how to get *"chicks for free."*

That was it.

I quietly and gently lifted the covers and glanced at the curvy naked body lying next to me.

Holy Shit!

We were both naked. Something must have happened. I wasn't sure who she was. I wasn't sure how I'd gotten there.

Opposite of most guys…I'd spent the beginning of my freshman year avoiding sexual confrontation. I was afraid of girls. Afraid. But, I'd become a smooth talker. I liked to talk. I liked to hear myself talk. I liked the attention I got when I said something funny or sounded kind of smart.

Girls didn't seem to notice my anxiety or sweaty palms. Maybe they noticed but they didn't say anything. Beer, and my quick wit had gotten me into some pretty deep kissing encounters. But, I always bailed, trying to avoid a repeat of the Summer hayride incident. It was never far from my mind.

Even though Summer had told me she'd never said those things about me, I'd still spent over a year thinking my breath was bad and I'd drooled on her. It was engrained in my memory as truth. I was pretty good at keeping myself at arm's length, until I had enough alcohol pulsing through my veins to cloud my judgment. I'd pissed off more than one classmate by leading her down the kissing, rubbing, heavy breathing road to nowhere.

But there I was. Had I done it? I must have. What other explanation was there for being in bed with a girl …butt-assed naked?

Who the fuck is she?

I silently reached out with my index finger.

Shit.

I touched her back. Barely. Enough. She breathed a heavy sigh and stretched her tan body.

Fuck.

Panic.

She rolled half toward me. Lean…and huge white boobs. I was sure I'd kneaded them like bread dough. I was sure of that, but not sure of anything else. She rolled all the way over. The silky sheet and plaid comforter fell the other way. My heart stopped for a full three seconds.

Are you kidding me?

I knew her. I'd talked to her a few times in passing and she'd been kind of flirty with me recently. She worked in town.

Holy shit….Her.

She was older. Like, out of school older. Way, way out of my league. So far out of my league. Here we were, naked in a strange bed, in a strange house. I had no idea what we'd done.

Who's fucking house is this?

Run.

I could feel my palms begin to moisten and I knew my pits were already doing their thing. I had to get off those shiny sheets. I had to get my clothes on and get the fuck out of that house before she woke up. After the initial rush of seeing her giant glowing boobs...I puked. Just inside the bedroom door.

My stomach rose into my mouth again, so I opened the nearest door. The bathroom. The toilet. Burning chunks of whatever I'd eaten the night before erupted from my throat. I heaved. Heaved. Heaved again. Every last drop of half-digested food and liquid and burning stomach acid that I had in me was now in the sparkling white bowl in front of me.

I wiped a long stringy spit from my lip and looked up into the half-open medicine cabinet mirror. There she was.

Still naked. Her face gave me no clue as to what was on her mind. I glanced down at her perfect vanilla boobs one more time, knowing that I'd probably never see them again.

I looked up and turned toward her.

Her expression hadn't changed.

Is she pissed?

Was she as confused as I was about what had gone on beneath those sheets the night before?

She called me by my last name. Watson. It felt like I was at football practice. Watson...I was pretty sure I'd just had sex with this person. Watson...it would be my first time. Watson...goddammit, did she even remember my first name?

"Watson, where are my clothes?"

"Not sure."

She turned and walked back toward the bed.

Damn!

I felt a sense of relief that it had finally happened. I felt a sense of awe that it was with her. But I also felt like I'd somehow fucked things up. She hadn't smiled.

After a few more minutes of dry-heaving, I wobbled over and leaned against the cold sink. A red tube of Closeup toothpaste stared at me from under a more than gently used washcloth. I still tasted the nastiness that had just made its escape from my stomach. I unscrewed the lid, rubbed a dot of clear red gel on my finger and put it on my tongue. I bent under the faucet and got a small sip of water and began swishing it around in my mouth. It foamed up quickly and I accidentally swallowed a little.

I puked.

My stomach settled down and I tried again, this time careful not to swallow any of the burning red foam. As I reached to turn off the water, I knocked the tiny white lid off the sink, watched it bounce off the little step stool between the sink and the toilet, and do three perfect flips as it cleared the lid and landed in the bowl...which I hadn't flushed yet.

Dammit! Shit! Fuck!

Luckily, the puke was thick enough to hold the lid on the surface.

Fuck.

I didn't want to touch the puke, or the pukey lid. I scanned the bathroom...nothing. I opened the drawer beneath the sink.

Voila. The shiny little tweezers stared up at me from between the hairbrush and a couple of lipstick cases.

I reached down and delicately grabbed the lid with the tweezers. I was pretty sure they'd never been used for this task before. Chunks of puke moved around on top of the water as I lifted the little white lid. It had landed sideways and had a tiny piece of potato chip stuck in the threads. The pungent smell of my digestive juices mixed with toilet water made my stomach rise again. I heaved, but nothing came up. I quickly rinsed the orange off the sides of the tiny lid and screwed it back on tightly. I put the tube back under the washcloth and decided it was time to go face the nakedness in the other room.

She wasn't there. She'd made the bed while I puked. She'd piled my clothes near the end, on the side where I'd woken up. The shades were open and I heard music playing from another room. Dire Straits again. Didn't the radio play any fucking thing else? I had to work hard not to puke again. My mouth was sandy and my head was swimming. I had to sit on the bed to put my clothes on. I didn't even remember wearing these clothes last night.

Damn, how much did I drink?

And where the fuck are my underwear?

I got my clothes on...minus underwear, finished buttoning the last button on my 501s, and walked in the other room. It was a mess. I avoided eye contact and kept the long couch between us.

"Where is everyone?"

"Tom's passed out in the other room and James took off." She said it without looking up.

"You should call James to come back and get you."

I looked out the window and finally realized where I was. I could walk home from here. It was only four blocks from my house.

She seemed mad. She was beautiful. She had her clothes on.

I felt like shit and didn't ask if she needed help cleaning up. I noticed one of the speakers making a fluffy sound as I walked toward the front door. It was blown. Probably Dire Straits.

My lips rubbed together like dry felt. I needed to puke again. My head was spinning and I heard Ratt cranking "Round and Round" as I stumbled down the front steps and into the bright mid-day sun.

I walked toward the shady part of the street. Pecan limbs drooped down over the road, not quite ready to drop their heavy fruit. I wasn't a virgin anymore. I was filled with both excitement and disappointment. She was smoking hot. I'd had sex with her. I couldn't remember a thing.

I made it home and walked up the front steps.

Fuck.

The front door was locked. No keys.

I walked around back door.

Double fucking fuck.

Locked.

I walked back around front and plopped down in the porch swing. I'd only been staring at the big tree for a minute or two when Mom pulled in the driveway.

I stood up as she opened her door and put a foot on the ground.

"Did you sleep well?" she asked. She grabbed her purse and banged the Suburban door closed.

"Yep," I said.

"I knocked on your door earlier for church, but decided to let you sleep," she said.

"Thanks," I said. "I locked myself out, just now."

She unlocked the door and I followed her in. The smell of roast assaulted my nose as I neared the kitchen. My stomach flipped a little. I'd only been up for a few minutes and couldn't even think about food yet. That scrumptious Sunday smell would have usually made my mouth water. It only made me queasy.

She was quiet as I followed her in.

Does she know I was out all night? She always seemed to know.

I turned on the light as I entered my room and immediately turned it back off. Too bright. I went straight to my bathroom and slurped some water from the sink. The cold water ran through my fingers. I tried to keep enough in the palm of my hand to rid my mouth of the cotton balls. It seemed extra bubbly as it ran through the small wire mesh filter on the end of the faucet. It wasn't wet enough.

I needed to feed my livestock. I was raising a show steer for Future Farmers of America and he had to eat, hangover or not. My head just wanted to lay down. My bed was there. The pillow beckoned. I stared at it for a long minute and gently swerved back and forth as the two thoughts fought for some kind of action.

Lay down.

Feed the steer.

My steer pen was tucked back behind Grandma's house. I didn't feel like making the walk, but it would give me an excuse to get away from Mom. I felt like she might start asking questions about the night before if I hung around any longer. Although I lied regularly, I always felt like a piece of shit about it. I didn't feel like lying now, so I figured today was a good day to clean the shit out of the pen. I'd clean it up good and spread some new hay for bedding.

I grabbed a Coke from the fridge on my way out. Fizz shot out like crazy when I popped the top. I guess I'd shaken it a bit. The cold foam made its way over my fingers and dripped off the bottom of the can on to the carpet. With a quick glance I was sure it didn't show up on our brown and rust colored shag.

"Don't slam the door," Mom yelled, as I made the bottom step.

The door slammed behind me.

The gravel at the end of the driveway crunched as I plodded across and stepped over the big pothole. It was still half-full from last week's rain. Oil from the road created a yellow and green rainbow sheen across the top.

I walked down the street toward Grandma's and looked toward his house. I still looked. Every time. Usually just a glance from the corner of my eye. And every time…the thought storm.

Is he the reason I always feel like something's wrong with me?

Is he the reason I get so nervous around girls?

Is he the reason I cut myself?

Other people didn't cut themselves…that much I knew.

Zeke's warm stare was waiting for me when I opened the first gate and headed for his pen. He watched for a few seconds and then began pacing the fence-line. He gave me a couple of raspy moos. The sound of his high-pitched voice always made me chuckle. He mooed again and began to pace faster as I got closer. I had the bucket of sweet molasses-covered feed I'd scooped from the bag in Grandma's garage. He knew what that green five-gallon bucket meant.

The thick white fur on his forehead muffled the sound of his head butting the gate as I tried to open it. He loved that feed. It was almost gone before I finished dumping it into the homemade wooden trough.

He also loved to go on walks. I stared up at the blue nylon halter.

I should take him.

My fucking head hurts.

I may puke.

As I looked at the halter I tried to piece together the events of the night before. I couldn't believe I'd finally been with a girl…and couldn't remember any of it. Nada. Nothing. Nil.

Zeke's long sandpapery tongue suddenly licked my arm. He licked me again and again. He started at my elbow and worked his way toward my wrist. He seemed to love licking salt off my skin any chance he got.

I sat on the trough and stroked his thick chocolate neck with my right hand while he licked my left.

"I got so fucked up last night."

"I woke up with this chick."

"She had giant boobs."

"I puked on the floor of the house down the street."

"Then I puked in the toilet."

"My fucking head hurts…no walk today."

He continued licking my hand and gave me another half-assed moo. I knew he understood. He always understood.

He was used to my voice. He was used to my stories. His energy was calm. His stare was non-judging. I told him stuff I'd never told anyone.

Stuff I hadn't told Mom or Dad. Stuff I hadn't told my teachers. Stuff I was sure I'd never tell anyone else. He'd heard it all. And he didn't care. He still loved me.

TWENTY-SIX

Monday morning.

Fuck.

I really wasn't ready to go back. The hangover was still rattling around in my head. I could still feel the remnants of cotton balls in my mouth. I didn't want to be around people.

I was thinking about the cut on my arm. Remembering how I'd eased down to the river after leaving the steer pen, and scratched it open, just a little. The blood had soaked through my sleeve and created a thin red line, just above the blue cuff of my short-sleeved shirt.

When Mom had seen the blood and seemed worried, I'd explained how I'd cut my arm on the top square of the bull-wire fence when reaching through to unlock the gate. I wondered if she noticed that I accidentally cut myself a lot. Had she noticed that it happened in different ways? Did it seem strange that it was always on the same arm, in exactly the same place?

I walked into the school parking lot. Tom was leaning back against his car with his arms crossed. He just stared. He looked mad. I couldn't imagine why.

We'd drank beer and rocked out in his car just two night ago, before I mysteriously ended up in a strange bed with a hot girl. So what the fuck was wrong with him today?

It wasn't that much out of the ordinary. He was always acting pissed about this or that, only to tell us he was just kidding later. He was always trying to convince us that he was unpredictable and crazy. It was really predictable.

126

The week before, he'd picked up a long grey night crawler and eaten it at football practice. He'd also been rumored to have bitten the head off a lizard. I didn't see that, so I wasn't sure I believed it. I didn't think he was crazy, just kind of stupid. He was my friend, but he seemed to need to intimidate me with his fake craziness every once in a while. I figured this was one of those days.

"Did you fuck her?" he asked abruptly.

It didn't register at first.

"Did you fuck her?"

"Who the hell are you talking about?" I asked.

"You know who I'm talking about," he said. "Did you fuck her?"

"Oh. The weekend. I did," I said. The left corner of my mouth turned up just a bit, creating a crooked little smile. "I did."

"Son-of-a-bitch," he said. "I planned on fucking her."

"Really?" I asked.

"Yeah, asshole. We went and grabbed another case of Bud and y'all were gone when we got back."

"We weren't gone. We were in the back bedroom."

We were in that bedroom naked. I was kneading bread dough, lots of bread dough, and I wasn't a virgin anymore.

"Well fuck," he said. "I guess I missed my chance."

"Yep."

"How was it?" he was half smiling now.

"Good," I lied. "Really good."

The bell rang, and we split up. My locker was on the far end of the hall, so I had to hurry.

Blood rushed into my cheeks as I turned the corner and walked into first period. Her younger sister sat right behind me. I'd totally forgotten about that. Embarrassed. Almost panic. I didn't know what girls told each other. Did she know I'd had sex with her sister? Did she know that her sister was my first?

"Hey," I said. I didn't make eye contact, just mumbled in her general direction. The teacher mumbled something too as he drew bad stick figures on the scratched-up chalk board.

She said something to one of my buddies who sat behind her. They were laughing. Her voice was just barely above a whisper. But some words were loud. It was as if she wanted me to hear some of what she was saying, but not everything. I strained my ears and caught part of their conversation.

"She was so disappointed on Saturday night," she said.

What the fuck?

Disappointed?

I tried to remember. Anything. Nothing.

"He didn't know what to do," she said, making damn sure I heard that part. "It's a shame there was so much to work with, but he didn't know what to do with it."

My insides imploded.

The faucet had turned on. My palms and pits were leaking.

They kept talking.

They kept laughing.

What the fuck?

Maybe I hadn't done it after all.

I knew it…something's wrong with me.

Fuck.

I had to go. I had to get out of there. I couldn't move.

I sat quietly with my head on my desk. My guts churned for the remainder of class. It was everything I could do to keep them down.

I was dazed. It was bad enough that I hadn't actually gone through with it, but the fact that she'd told people made me burn. Made my whole body burn. I felt my eyes welling up as people smiled at me in the hall. I noticed faint laughter and snickering in my periphery but didn't acknowledge it.

I tried even harder to remember—to piece together enough of the story to know what had happened. It just wouldn't come together. I couldn't remember anything after drinking some beer in Tom's car.

Blank. It was the first time that had ever happened. Complete blackout. Nothing. All I knew was I'd woken up next to the boobs.

I'd heard other guys laughing and joking about being too drunk to do this or that, but it felt different. We weren't laughing together. We weren't all joking around about how drunk I'd been and what I'd done, or not done. Hell, I didn't know what I'd done or not done. They were laughing at me. They thought I was an idiot. I was sure that she thought I was an idiot too.

That stung the most. I'd felt so lucky to wake up next to her. I'd wanted her to be the first.

She not only thought I was an idiot...she felt the need to tell her sister and all of her friends. My friends.

The week drug by. Slowly. Painfully.

By the time Saturday rolled around, I was exhausted. My chest hurt when I thought of all the laughter and mocking I'd just endured. It was the worst week of my life.

All my friends, and some people I didn't consider friends, had kept the conversation going all week. Different versions of that night. Snippets through laughter and disgust. I hadn't done it. I didn't know how to do it.

I held the nail in my right hand, anticipating the joyous pain I was about to be blessed with. I held it there. Shiny. Glistening. Recently sharpened. An inch from my skin. I didn't move it closer. I just looked at my arm.

That little boat dock. That muddy river. It had become one of my most frequented spots. Just me. Always me. Sometimes my sharpened nail. Sometimes not. The river flowed by. Muddy grey water. Always there.

I held my eyes on the small reddish scar. The tiny remnant of scab left over from the last time. The thin red line. My release. My pain. My control.

That fucking bitch.

I didn't want her to be my first anyway.

I stared into the water. I was tired of thinking. I wondered what it would feel like to slide down into that beautifully warm water and just breath in. I imagined myself sinking down as far as I could. Sinking down to where the warm water met the cold. Sinking down, just out of sight, and breathing in. One long, slow, wet, warm breath. I could do that. I wanted to do that. No one other than my family would even know I was gone. No one would care.

TWENTY-SEVEN

I never quite lived that one night down. One drunken night where I may or may not have lost my virginity to a girl with big white boobs and an even bigger mouth. That fucking night came back up in conversations many times. My whole freshman year was agonizing. Maybe it was because the subject hit a hot spot for me. I began to believe that all my friends were just assholes. They were just a bunch of virgins that felt better making fun of someone who almost wasn't a virgin anymore. Maybe none of them were virgins, and they just thought I was a joke. At least I'd woken up next to a hot naked girl. At least.

I stayed drunk and avoided any situation with a potential for failure. At work, at home, or with girls, I was careful to keep myself out of the deep water. I had more than one crush, and more than one girl liked me back. I was just too afraid to do anything about it. Something was wrong with me, deep down inside. Really wrong. The sweating had gotten worse and the kerosene smelling medicine I put on my hands daily didn't really work. I hated school and I hated myself…when I wasn't able to have some beers.

TWENTY-EIGHT

Lying in my room counting lines in the wood grain paneling on my wall, I contemplated the summer as it came to an end.

Drunk. I'd stayed drunk for most of it. There'd been lake trips. I'd gone to the beach. My buddies and I had driven almost every back road within twenty miles of home.

Sad. A subtle sense of sadness blanketed everything I did. I wanted to have fun. Everyone around me seemed to be having fun. Laughing. Drinking. Fucking. It all seemed great. I just couldn't get there.

I was about to be a sophomore and I looked at the upcoming school year with dread. Freshman year had been a bust. One drunk night had defined my whole fucking existence for the whole fucking year.

Why would this year be any different?

I was rolling around in these thought when Dad walked in to my room.

"We're going to look at a truck for you this afternoon," he said.

"What?"

"A truck. You need one."

"Yeah, I do."

"A guy near Austin has one and we're going to go look at it."

Since I had just turned fifteen, and since I was still working at the locker plant, I could get my hardship driver's license. The usual age was sixteen, but since I had a steady job I could get mine early.

Most of the people in my grade were older than me, and already had their licenses. It seemed that having a license and a car of their own had instantly turned them into cool people. I wouldn't have to walk to school, or wait on a friend, who may or may not show up, to give me a ride.

The driving part was easy. I'd been driving Old Blue out in the hay field and on little country roads since I was ten or twelve years old. Paw Paw even let me drive through town and all the way to his house on occasion.

Hyper excitement kept my foot bouncing on the floorboard as Dad and I drove down to the neighboring town to check out the truck.

"What color is it?"

"Tan. The man said it was tan."

It was sitting there in the driveway when we drove up.

"Holy shit," I said. "It looks brand new."

I jumped out before Dad had a chance to come to a complete stop. I walked around it slowly. I ran my hands across the smooth paint on the passenger side door. The sun reflected off the shiny hood as I pretended to inspect it.

My chest was about to explode.

Holy shit.

Is Dad going to buy this for me?

It was the same basic truck as Old Blue. It was just newer, shinier, and all mine.

Emotions welled up suddenly and my eyes filled with water. I turned my head as the guy in the beat-up feed-store cap explained exactly what we'd be getting. He emphasized the vowels as he spoke.

"1984 Chevy Silverado four-by-four with a 350 engine and a four-barrel carburetor," he said. "It's tall and tan. It has 4-on-the-floor and brand new all-terrain tires all the way around."

"Looks okay," Dad said.

Okay…Are you fucking kidding me?

"It also had less than twenty-thousand miles on the odometer," the old man added.

"Yeah," Dad countered.

"It's real clean," the man said. "Why don't you take it around the block?"

When I turned the key, the starter kicked and the motor was almost silent. Just a glorious hum.

"Let's take a drive," Dad said. "It is clean. Real clean."

I made the block without noticing anything around me. Everything was invisible except that beautiful brown dash and the shiny head on the shifter.

"What's your price?" Dad stepped out quickly when we rolled back into the driveway.

Their voices were quiet as they walked around the back and dickered. Muffled words, but I could tell Dad was trying to get him down a little.

It was perfect.

I didn't need to see or hear anything else.

Dad walked around the driver's side, where I was still sitting.

"It's yours."

I jumped out and hugged his neck.

It was mine. Mine.

This will make me cool.

My chest was so swollen it almost touched the steering wheel as I drove up to the food locker that Saturday morning. I couldn't wait for Matt to see it.

I walked in.

"Come outside," I said.

"Why?" he asked.

"Just come outside," I said again.

He acted surprised when he stepped out of the back door.

"So now you can haul me around everywhere," he said.

"Hell yeah," I replied. I could barely contain my excitement.

Then, to my surprise, he went over to his truck and grabbed something out of the back. I wasn't sure what the hell it was, but when he walked back over, I was floored. The only thing my truck had been missing were Chevy brand hubcaps. The previous owner had lost them or put them on another vehicle. It only had bare white rims.

Matt walked over and started putting hubcaps on the front wheels.

What the hell?

"How'd you know?" I asked.

How the hell did he even know I got a new truck?

"I talked to your dad. He told me yesterday," he said.

He'd also happened to have four Chevy hubcaps lying around, since his monster truck had gigantic wheels and regular hubcaps wouldn't fit them.

The morning just wouldn't go by fast enough. The clock seemed to tick extra slow and extra loud. We weren't very busy, which just made the time go by even slower.

I tried to watch the clock without Matt noticing. I glanced up out of the corner of my eye. I glanced back down at the crinkled white sheet of freezer paper I'd just torn off the large roll. I plopped a one-pound ball of hamburger meat in the center and was about to wrap it up. Matt laughed. When I looked up at him, he laughed again.

"Why don't you just go out there and sit in the mother fucker," he asked.

"What?"

"You aren't getting much done." He was smiling.

"Sorry," I said. "I just can't stop thinking about it."

We worked until noon, jumped in my new ride, and cruised the Y for about an hour. Confidence welled up in my chest. I was grown. I was alive. The feeling of freedom became stronger and stronger as I cruised back and forth on the same piece of road, over and over.

I waved and people waved back, even though they weren't sure who was waving at them. After a few waves, they caught on and realized it was me. James and Tom pulled me over and wanted to check out the truck. I made the block and met them on the back side. I popped the hood. I pointed out the new tires. I didn't miss any details as I explained why it was so bad-ass. They actually seemed impressed.

On Monday, I was a mix of excitement and nerves. It would be the first time I showed up to school in my own vehicle. It was kind of a rite of passage. The move from walking or catching rides to driving up in your own ride. I cruised the Y a few times before school. I didn't see anyone else, but it didn't matter much. I had the windows down. I had the music up. Sammy Hagar blasted "I Can't Drive 55", as I cruised back and forth on the 35 mile per hour strip of pavement.

I made it through two more songs and headed to school. I rewound the Hagar song, made the corner, and found a spot. I pulled slowly into the first convenient parking space - a dirt area where no one else was parked. No lines. No curbs.

When I glanced up, a couple of older guys coming my way.

They walked over and checked out the truck for a few minutes. They talked fast about engines and gears and carbs. I didn't let on that I had no clue what the hell they were talking about. I just nodded and acted like we were all on the same page.

"You wanna come to a party on Saturday?" one of the guys asked.

"Hell yeah," I said.

"Out on Loop Road," he said. "In the big pasture."

It was a great truck. An unfamiliar feeling surfaced…

I fit in.

I got in my truck and turned the key. The smell of cherries wafted from the AC vents, and The Cars sang "Let the Good times Roll" as I pulled away from another party in the big pasture. I'd had my truck for a few months and partied out there almost every weekend. The new had worn off a bit. That first party, that first weekend driving my own truck had been the greatest. Excitement mixed with pride. Everyone staring as I drove in the gate that first time.

I left this time the same way I always did. The same way we all did. In the front gate. Out the side gate.

The huge oak tree stood to my left as I rumbled down Loop Road and neared the little railroad crossing east of Ship's Lake. Gravel flew from my back tires as I punched the gas and got back on the highway.

She's gonna hate me.

She was laying naked in Blake's car…waiting for me.

She's probably still there.

All I'd had to do was walk down the small hill, climb in that car, and get busy.

What the fuck is wrong with me?

I'd been a little confused when Blake explained it.

"Dude are you sure?" I asked.

"Positive," he said.

"How do you know?"

"She said so," he replied. "And she was already taking her clothes off when I closed the door."

I'd known her forever. She'd never acted like she liked me. At least not "liked me" liked me. It didn't make any sense. She was a really good friend.

But Blake was sure. He'd been my good buddy since the beginning of the year and I trusted his word.

"She's waiting. Naked."

I couldn't. Panic set in. A heavy crushing panic. I just couldn't.

So, I'd bailed.

I'd had a few beers and felt warm, light and happy. Then he'd told me she was there.

Bees in my stomach. Bees in my throat. I held them down, but barely. A few more beers and maybe I'd have fucked her.

But, I wasn't drunk enough yet. Not yet.

The headlights made the gravel road look orange as I turned left and headed for my favorite back road.

As soon as I was out of sight I stopped. I arched my back, reached through the sliding back window, and opened my little red Igloo. My hand went numb as I sank it into the stinging ice and felt around for the perfect bottle.

It was usually bottles. I'd drink cans when someone else was buying, but I really liked bottles. I drank Miller Lite when I was with Matt, but when it was just me, I drank Bud Light…long neck bottles. I closed my fingers around the neck and pulled the amber container out of the icy water. The last few ice-cubes dropped off as I pulled it in and closed the window. I shoved it down into my Panama Jack koozie.

A stream of air and icy water shot through the little hole on the bottom. My index finger already had little slices from opening the twist tops during the evening. I added one more. My breath quickened as the little drift of steam rose from the top of the bottle. I took the first sip…and the rubber band in my shoulders relaxed. Maybe I'd drink a few more and venture back to the party. She might still be waiting in that car for me. Probably not. But, maybe.

I rode around by myself for about an hour, avoiding town because I knew there'd be folks wanting to jump in and cruise. I wouldn't mind so much, except I didn't feel like sharing my beer, or talking, or anything. These sullen moods were hitting me more often, and it took eight or ten beers before I came out of my shell.

I hung around people. Smiled. Laughed. Tried to fit in. The feeling that something was wrong with me was always there. It only went away when I calmed the tornado. And the only way I'd found to do that, without drawing blood from myself, was consuming large quantities of beer, or whiskey, or screwdrivers, or trashcan punch, or anything else that anyone had available.

One bottle. Five bottles. Eight bottles. I decided I was going back to find the naked girl in the car.

As I made a wide corner, I heard my tires wailing. The mud-grips made a kind of skipping howl as they bounced and skidded across the slick asphalt. I barely stayed with it through the turn. My correction was just enough to keep me out of the ditch on the other side of the road. Downshifting into third, I punched it and hit the straightaway. Def Leppard screamed "Me and My Wine" as I reached sixty. Seventy. Eighty miles per hour. I was almost out of road, but I wanted to hit a hundred before I let off the gas. I thought I had just enough pavement to make it.

I did not.

The stop sign appeared out of nowhere. I knew it was too late, even as I slammed on the brakes. They locked. The tires howled as I hit the near side of the deep ditch. The truck was air-born...but not for long. I hit the other side of the ditch with a jolt and my head rattled back and forth like a bobble-head doll. My bottom lip hit the steering wheel, and then the whole truck bounced. Once. Twice. And stopped.

I'd hit something pretty solid but couldn't see anything from inside the truck. I panicked. Was it a cow? Was it a barn? A house? I had no idea, but I knew I had to get the fuck out of there.

I ground the shifter back in reverse and stepped on the gas. The tires spun. The smell of burning rubber filled the cab as they made a valiant effort to grip the loose soil and rock. I'd ran it up on a mound and the back wheels were barely touching the rocks. Enough to make noise and cause smoke, but not enough to grab hold so I could flee the scene.

What the hell?

What should I do?

I could walk to town and find somebody to pull me out. I could walk over to the nearby houses and ask for help. A vicious, snarling barrage of barking ruled that option out right away.

What the fuck?

I remembered that my truck had four-wheel drive.

I jumped out and walked around the front of the truck.

Barbed wire gleamed in the beam of my left headlight. The right one was broken. The twisted wire was stretched across the front bumper and over part of the hood.

Fuck.

I'd broken through a fence and hit a thick mass of vines and underbrush. No large trees, but enough solid stuff to do some damage.

My mind scrambled. I couldn't worry about the damage right then. I had to get that wire off my bumper, lock in the four-wheel drive hubs, and get the hell out of there. I spun the left hub and walked around to the right side. Tangled limbs and grass were wrapped around the tire and jammed under the fender. I couldn't see the wheel. My arms tired as I pulled and yanked and cussed. The cussing must have helped. I broke enough of the vegetation loose to reach the hub. I spun it and ran around the back.

Fuck.

I forgot about the ditch and landed on my face. Rocks. Dewberry vines. Mud.

My hands sank up to the wrists in the muck as I pushed myself up. A thousand little dewberry thorns bit at each palm. They tore a thousand little holes in my hands as I tried to wipe them off on my pants. The only thing that came off was the mud. I stumbled back up the bank and finally climbed in my truck. I noticed the spilled cooler in the bed and grabbed another beer. I'd planned to get more ice before they got too warm and I needed to find somebody to buy some more...I only had four left.

With both hubs locked, and the truck in four-high, I was able to make it back out through the ditch. There was just enough contact between the ground and the front wheels to get me started. I almost buried it climbing the far side. Luckily it was a bit more solid than the field side and my all terrain tires got enough traction to pull me up and over.

Once on safe ground, or safe pavement, I assessed the damage. My truck was a mess. Wire, limbs, and thorny vines had left deep, jagged scratches on my beautiful tan paint job. The front left fender had a watermelon-sized dent. The center of the hood had one to match. Dad was gonna kill me.

Whose fucking fence was that?

Now what?

Busted lip. Thorny hands. Muddy jeans. Scratched and dented

hood and fenders. Broken headlight. Warming beer.

I wasn't ready to go home and face the parents. Even drunk, I knew I couldn't drive through town with my fucked-up truck, and one headlight. Only one thing to do. I slammed another beer and headed out on my original mission…find the naked girl in the car.

The noise woke me. Bang. Knock. Bang

What the fuck?

I cracked my eyes for a look around. An open window. My window.

I never open that window.

Clothes strewn across the floor between there and my bed. They looked like mine. The comforter was on me. Sheets were on the floor.

Headache. Stabbing behind my eyes.

What was that fucking noise?

"Can you unlock the door?" Dad asked.

Oh shit.

I must have stayed out too late. Maybe snuck in my window. I prepared myself for the obligatory "You stayed out too late" speech.

I got one foot on the floor and slid the other one down slowly. A wave of water sloshed from one side of my head to the other as I tried to stand. I quickly sat back down on the edge of the bed.

Fuck. What happened to my hands?

I didn't have time to assess them.

"Can you unlock the door?" he asked again.

I never locked that door.

I stood up and shuffled across the carpet. I opened the door with a start. Dad usually didn't look that pissed. I told him I'd been riding around and must have lost track of time. He just dropped his head.

"Follow me," he said.

"Where?" I asked.

"Just follow me." He headed for the front door.

The concrete porch felt cool on the bottoms of my bare feet. I looked out and saw my truck parked in the yard. At first, I was as shocked as Dad must have been when he first saw it. It was beat to shit.

After a few seconds of confusion, it all came back to me. The naked girl. All those fucking beers. The back roads. The Def Leppard. The hauling ass. The tires wailing and bouncing. The crash. The vines and mud and wire and broken headlight and dents and scratched paint and thorns and…my hands. Red. Scratched. Muddy. A pincushion of tiny little thorns jutted out from the palms.

"Let's go," he said.

"Where?"

"Out where you did that to your truck."

"How do you know where?"

"The landowner is a friend of mine," he said. "Your wallet was in the ditch."

I tried but couldn't make eye contact. He was mad. But more than that, he was embarrassed. I'd embarrassed him again.

"Let me put on some shoes," I said.

Where the fuck are my shoes?

The ride out to the big ditch took forever. Cotton balls strangled me and I wished I'd brought some water. Swish swish swishing in my ears drowned out the country song on the radio. Dad stared straight ahead.

He slowed the truck as we pulled up to the site.

"What the hell happened?" Dad asked.

"I was driving a little too fast," I answered.

"A little?" he eyed me with a familiar suspicious look.

The two long shiny black skid marks on the pavement indicated that it was more than just a little. I'd jumped the ditch and torn the shit out of someone's fence…that part was obvious just by looking. I remembered most of it, but it had been dark. I'd been drunk. The scene looked worse than I remembered.

"It wasn't my fault," I said bluntly. "I dropped my Van Halen cassette on the floorboard and reached down to get it."

He handed me the muddy wallet I'd dropped and got his fence repair tools out of the back of his truck.

"You can dig the holes," he said without looking up. He must have loaded all the supplies before waking me.

The sun beamed and my head swam. I robotically jammed the post hole digger down into the ground. The gravelly soil was still wet, so the digging wasn't that hard. Up. Hold. Down. Up. Hold. Down.

After what seemed like an hour, I was finally finishing up the last hole.

"Just how fast were you going?" he finally spoke again.

"Not sure," I said. "I wasn't paying attention."

"Well it looks like you were going way too fast," he said.

"Yeah. It won't happen again," I said.

His voice gave away his anger. But the lines on his forehead gave away much more. He was worried about me.

We set the last post and stretched the new pieces of wire we'd precut. I hated that he was mad. But even more, I hated that I'd let him down again. I'd embarrassed him again.

"This is the third wreck in two months," he said. "Seems like every Sunday morning it's something else."

"I know," I said. "I'm not sure why this shit keeps happening to me."

Silence.

"I'll take it easy from now on."

TWENTY-NINE

"You ready, bitch?" Tom yelled.

"Fuck yeah," I said. "It's Saturday isn't it?"

He was standing on a chair and held the funnel as high above his head as he could. It had only been two weeks since I'd crashed my truck through the fence and told Dad I'd take it easy on the drinking. Yet, here I was.

"Do it, fucker," I yelled. My voice was high and hoarse. I'd been yelling all night.

"Do it."

My thumb slid off the bottom end of the tube. All three beers shot down my throat in a matter of seconds. There was only a swishing sound. I gulped twice, maybe three times, and it was gone. As always, some of the beer shot out the sides as my cheeks expanded, but not enough to matter.

Tom tossed the funnel on the grass next to me and jumped on someone's back. I looked down at it. Even though I'd made it myself only a few weeks before, I still smiled every time I saw it. I'd covered the blue Napa oil funnel with Miller Light and Bud Light stickers. Lots of people had signed their name, or wrote something dirty, with a black Magic Marker. A three-foot long piece of clear tubing extended from the bottom. It was long enough to allow the person holding it to get high enough for gravity to really push the beer down the drinker's throat. It could hold three beers, as long as they didn't foam too much.

Now for the hard part…trying to hold down those three beers.

I felt my stomach lurch once, twice. I made myself sit down and breathe. No one wanted to waste three beers. Puking after the funnel was considered pretty weak and I didn't want to appear weak. I held it down.

Tom's girlfriend had brought a girlfriend to the party. I knew her from school. I had her in a couple of classes.

"You're the hottest chick here," I whispered in her ear.

"Oh, really?" she asked.

"Yep," I said. "It's not even close."

After a few minutes, I talked her in to hitting the funnel. Then, I hit it again.

We drank beer. We drank some Jim Beam straight from the bottle. We drank some cheap ass dry wine…one of those big half-gallon bottles…*Cella* something or other. We drank some more beer and flirted. My head was spinning. I felt great.

We jumped in the pool. She grabbed a handful of my thick hair and yanked our faces together. I kissed her like I'd never kissed anyone. Her tongue was warm. Her mouth was wet. The faint taste of menthol cigarettes lingered between us.

We drank. We drank some more. She strategically moved her hands under the water and into my shorts. She got the reaction she wanted.

"I'll be in your truck," she said.

"I'll grab some beers and meet you there," I said.

Some of the guys were watching as I stacked as many beers in my arms as I could carry.

"Have fun, fucker," Tom said. "Leave us some beer."

I just smiled and let the shitty wooden gate slam behind me.

She was waiting in my truck when I opened the door. She grabbed my hair again as soon as I jumped up and landed on the seat. Our mouths locked together until I had to come up for a breath.

"Where to?" I asked.

"Doesn't matter," she said. "Away from all these people."

"Okay," I said. "Hang on."

She was glued to my side as I punched the gas and spun dirt and grass out behind us. Her warm hand gripped the inside of my thigh as we cruised the Y a few times. I wanted everyone to see me cruising around with her next to me.

As we neared the east end of town she looked over at me.

"Let's go," she said.

I didn't have to ask. I knew what she meant.

The Park was only a couple miles away. We had the windows down and AC/DC was booming "Highway to Hell" through my six-by-nines. The bass thumped hard against that homemade wooden speaker box.

The little two-track dirt path appeared out of nowhere and angled into the piney woods from the main road. She grabbed the wheel and yanked it to the right. The truck swerved sideways and barely made the opening.

We'd only gone a few yards when she reached over and stomped on the brake. We both slammed forward and sideways. My face almost hit the dashboard. Dust drifted into the open windows. I exaggerated my cough and we laughed.

"Fuck," I said.

"Okay," she replied.

She took off all of her clothes.

We kissed.

We drank another beer.

We kissed some more. It was different with her. Her lips invited me. Her tongue held me there.

Suddenly, she climbed on top of me and pulled my shirt off. I wasn't nervous. I felt awesome. And it was the first time I'd ever felt awesome with a girl. I was drunk enough to tame my anxiety, but not drunk enough to keep me from functioning.

I fumbled with the buttons on my Levis. I somehow got them off with her still straddling me. My hands moved across her body like they'd been there a thousand times. Her back was warm. Her smooth skin an invitation.

We laid down in the seat.

We kissed.

Our bodies moved.

We kissed.

She stared into my eyes.

We moved.

We kissed and moved and kissed and moved. I wanted it to last all night. I knew it wouldn't. I felt it. She must have sensed it.

"Don't stop," she said.

So I didn't. I just kept moving.

But only for another thirty seconds or so. Electricity shot though my body. I jerked and shook and jerked. Then, I collapsed and just laid there. Her breath was heavy beneath me.

Silence for a while. Tree frogs sang in the oaks. Wind moaned ever so slightly through the open windows.

"Is it okay that I came in you," I asked. I'd heard plenty of conversations between the other guys about leaving it on a rag or sock or shirt or seat. But to never, ever do it in her.

"I'm on the pill," she said with a laugh. And then she kissed me. For a long time.

"I'm not quite done," she said.

I didn't know what that meant. I was done.

She slid her head down into my lap. I wasn't quite done after all.

Grabbing.

Scratching.

Sweating.

Growling.

It seemed to last for hours. We moved. Once we found a rhythm…we just moved. But this time we didn't kiss. We just moved and moved and moved.

Her moans were raspy and deep. She let out a high-pitched yell. Louder and louder. Faster and faster.

Her body seized. Her nails dug into my upper back. My body seized. We shook and jerked together. She went limp.

She was spent.

I was spent.

We laid there. I hadn't noticed that the radio was on. The wind was cool on my bare feet as they hung out of the passenger side door. Helix sang "Deep Cuts the Knife" while we soaked in each other's energy, tangled together on that tan leather seat.

The pines and oaks were dancing in the moonlight. Twinkling stars seemed to blink on and off through the moving gaps in the forest canopy. I wanted to tell her that I loved her. I wanted to say the words.

The curves and lines of her naked body were just visible in the moonlight. Her eyes were locked on me. Glowing. Green. I hadn't paid attention before.

I was sure she heard my heart pounding as we breathed each other in, thinking our own thoughts.

Does she know she's my first?

I knew I wasn't hers. I didn't care.

Did I do it right this time?

I knew I had.

I knew in that moment that I'd never forget her.

We sorted out the bundle of clothes on the sandy floorboard, got dressed and decided to head back in to town. I felt electric. I was free. I was a normal guy.

This was what it was supposed to be like. This was how it was supposed to happen. I was supposed to feel just like this.

I was ready to rock. I was ready to take on all comers.

Bring on the world.

It's time to celebrate.

It didn't matter if anyone else knew what we were celebrating. I didn't care at all. I jumped out before we got back on the main road. My hand slid beneath the icy surface of the water in my Igloo. I sloshed it around, looking for the perfect beer. Found it. Grabbed two more.

I shoved in my *7800 Fahrenheit* cassette, rewound it to "In and Out of Love", and stepped on the gas. We were off. The screeching tires spun as we did two donuts at the small intersection. I ground the shifter to third, and laid rubber as we hauled ass back toward the city lights. Her hair tickled my neck as the wind whipped it this way and that.

As we rolled back into town, drinking beer and blasting music, my chest was bursting with happiness. I'd never felt anything like this. I was driving my very own truck. My arm was around the beautiful girl sitting next to me and her hand was on my leg. If my buddies asked if I'd fucked her, I could assure them that I had. I was goddamn sure this time. It was the best night of my life.

I felt like driving fast and doing something crazy. I couldn't remember ever feeling that free.

"Hell fucking yes," I yelled out the window.

"Hell fucking yes," she yelled even louder.

We blew through town doing eighty. I went down a side road about fifty miles too fast and before I knew it, I'd jumped a ditch and was in a big field. Moonlight made the blonde grass look like snow.

She looked at me with a devilish smile.

"What the hell are you smiling at?" I asked.

"You chicken?" she asked back.

I assured her I was not, slammed it in gear and punched the gas.

The tan Chevy bounced and swerved as we flew around the edges of the field. The tires started to lose traction and mud was flying up and around the open windows. Against my better judgement, I decided to drive straight through the middle of the snowy expanse.

The hubs were not locked in four-wheel drive, but I figured I could make it anyway. We started losing speed about halfway through. The pedal was already on the floor. Mud flew off all four wheels. Water and mud from a huge puddle splashed up and back down again. The windshield went dark. I couldn't see anything. The wipers only smeared the brown chocolate icing from side to side.

I couldn't stop. We'd surely sink. After a few seconds, the wipers finally made some headway. The other side of the field appeared in the dim muddy headlight beams. There was a ditch, but not as deep as the one we flew over when we entered.

"Hang on," I yelled.

It was too late. Our heads made a simultaneous thud as they hit the roof. The truck bounced up and down two more times., but when it finally came to rest, we were back on solid ground.

"Holy fuck," I shouted.

"Holy fuck is right," she said.

We found ourselves in each other's arms again. She stopped laughing when I kissed her. Gravel shot out behind us as we climbed the little hill toward town. It was steep but not very tall.

We crested the hill. We'd made it.

Then, we noticed a truck blocking the road. I slammed on the brakes. The black Chevy sat there, its bright shining eyes staring us down. I recognized the truck. We were fucked.

I sat there, scared. I thought about slamming it in reverse and taking our chances backing down the hill. But what good would that do? They knew my truck. They had probably sat and watched us tear up the field. I wasn't at all sure who's field it was, but I knew the blonde fuckers inside that black truck. They weren't letting us get by them without a confrontation.

As I eased forward and pulled up next to them, the smoke from their cigarettes made its way over to us. I played the whole incident off and tried to act cheery.

"What's up dudes?" I asked. "Y'all drink any beer tonight?"

"Yeah, little man," the older brother said. His ugly teeth added snarl to his words.

"You must be pretty fucked up to be tearing up that field down there like that," the younger one chimed in.

"Yeah, why else would anybody be that stupid," the older one said.

"I didn't know it belonged to anyone," I said.

"So you think all that fuckin' hay just planted itself?" older one again.

"You're fucked, little man," the younger one said. "We watch that field for the owner and helped him plant all that fuckin' hay." He kind of laughed.

"We saw your whole little dance," the older one said. "The donuts, the jumps, and the way you fucked it all up."

They'd seen the entire I'm Not a Virgin Anymore celebration.

I sat there and stared back at these two fucking assholes trying to ruin my night. They had no idea what we'd done earlier. They looked at her, then at me, and smiled.

"Enjoy it while you can, little man," one of them said.

"Yeah, the owner will be in touch," the other snapped.

My fear began to subside. They were just drunk assholes. I didn't really care what they saw or what they thought or who they told. I didn't care who the owner was. Fuck them all.

"Fuck you," I said, after I'd pulled out of earshot.

We blew it off and headed toward town.

Nothing was going to ruin this night. Nothing.

THIRTY

Ringing. My eyes wouldn't open. Ringing. The quilt felt heavy on my side. My quilt. I was home. I was in my bed.

"Yes, he's here," Mom said.

"Who is it?" I heard Dad's voice.

"They didn't say," she replied.

His chair scraped the linoleum floor as he slid it out from under the kitchen table. A comforting sound. He was home and not out on a train somewhere. His voice was monotone as he answered someone's questions. He spoke softly. I could barely make out what he was saying.

I wasn't really awake. I was in what had become a familiar Sunday morning state. Headache. Eyes glued shut. stomach ready to bail at the slightest movement. Badly hung-over...again.

The tap on my sliding bedroom door was soft. I'd fallen back asleep while he was talking.

"Did you drive your truck through someone's hayfield last night?" he asked.

"Fuck. I mean yeah. I think so. Maybe," I said.

Fuck. Those fucking blonde assholes ratted me out.

I'd only been home for a couple hours. Those guys had given me no slack for having a hot girl with me. They'd had no clue that I was celebrating.

CELEBRATING.

Holy shit.

I got laid.

I'm not a virgin anymore.
I'd did it.
I definitely remembered it.
"Get dressed," he said. "We've got work to do."

The drive out to the rutted pasture wasn't long enough. My stomach flipped and I focused on keeping its contents down. I moved the shovel up and down, back and forth. It seemed to swing forward on its own, scoop the sand, and pitch it to the right and into the ruts I'd created the night before. Even though Dad had been saying some words on the short ride over from our house, I still wasn't fully awake...or sober. He stuck around and helped for a half-hour or so.

"Finish on your own," he said. "I'll come back and check on you later."

"Okay."

"The owner isn't filing charges," he said. He stared into the distance.

"That's good," I replied. I couldn't think of anything else to say.

Droplets of sweat ran down my forehead and into my eyes. I wiped it away as I watched him drive slowly up the same hill I'd rutted up the night before. The day was turning out to be scorching hot.

I leaned on the shovel and stared at the ruts. I'd really fucked up that field.

A thin smile creased the corner of my mouth. Memories from the night before flooded in. The tan bench seat. The moonlight. Her naked body. Moving. Moaning. Scratching.

Shoveling's not that bad.
Fuck those assholes.
Then, I threw up.

THIRTY-ONE

I waited for her answer with baited breath.

"I know I'm only fifteen, but all of my friends are going," I pleaded. "I have a ride lined up."

"No," she said.

"I know it's a bachelor party but there won't be strippers."

"No." Her jaw muscles flexed.

"I'll be home by one."

"No." she said.

The bachelor was a family friend, and everyone I knew would be there. But, fucking up that field, and embarrassing Mom and Dad the weekend before had gotten me technically grounded. I'd been grounded all week. If it had been the first time I'd missed curfew, I might have had a chance. It wasn't. I shouldn't even have been asking.

"Simon really wants me to ride with him," I said.

She walked back toward my room. The frown lines on her forehead became more creased as she spoke.

"No," she said. "You can't go."

No matter that it was Friday night. No matter that it was the biggest party of the year. The black snakey hoses and shiny round pump handles would just be waiting for us when we walked up. Kegs. Free beer. Gallons of it.

"Everybody's going to be there," I said, not quite ready to give up.

"That doesn't matter," she answered flatly.

"They're all expecting me," a sense of panic churned in my gut.

"That doesn't matter either." Her shoulders tensed and moved closer to her ears.

"I won't have any friends left if I don't go." My pitch got higher.

"No," she said. "Just, no." She let out one long breath.

My insides were about to come out. My heart banged in my ears like a hammer. My chest pounded and my stomach churned like our homemade ice cream maker. The contents of my whole body were spinning round and round...from my head to my toes.

Desperation.

"No," she said again, just as I was about to open my mouth.

"Fuck this shit," I said reflexively. The words had come from nowhere.

Although I cussed like a drunken sailor around my friends, I never cussed in front of Mom. It must have caught her off guard. She didn't reply. She just stared as I stepped around her and slammed my sliding door behind me. Without looking back, I slammed the back door.

She didn't yell don't slam the door. She didn't yell anything.

I hadn't left the house all week, thinking it may buy me a ticket to the party on Friday. It didn't. I was a prisoner. She had my truck keys. I had no beer.

Fuck.

I'll just be sitting in my shitty old house watching some shitty old T.V.
All my friends will be drinking fizzy fucking beer from keg hoses.
I know there'll be strippers.
Goddammit.

Wild horses were stomping on my guts as I eased my way down the hill, through the grass that I should have already mown. Long Bermuda grass stems and sticker burs lapped over the trail just before it wound down the steep part of the bank. The trail hadn't seen much use. The river hadn't called me down in a while. I'd been drunk a lot. I even drank a beer or two during the week when my insides started swirling. Mom didn't know when football practice was over, so I sometimes drank a couple while cruising the Y. Spearmint gum was my cover, it never failed me.

The bottoms of my white high tops became caked with mud as I squish-squashed along the lower part of the trail. I wiped most of it off on a fallen log, leaving two shoe-shaped gravelly brownies on the soft spongy bark.

After cleaning the shoes, I began to walk in the grass just to the side of the narrow dirt path, trying to avoid the sticky mud.

Fuck this shit.

Fuck Mom and Dad.

Fuck Simon and any of my friends that ride with him.

Fuck it all.

A tinge of guilt worked its way up from my chest and got stuck in my head. It was all my fault. Driving my truck through that field the week before had been stupid. Missing curfew again had been stupid. But, I'd done things with her that I never had. I'd done everything right…she'd confirmed it to my friend's girlfriend the next night. I'd been good. I'd been great.

But now, regret overshadowed everything else. Simon and the other guys would be laughing and joking and driving that big white boat of a car out there on that country road with the windows down and Krokus blasting "Midnite Maniac". I knew he'd be playing that song. He always played that song. I so wanted to see a stripper in real life. I wanted to drink my weight in free beer.

Goddammit.

Why am I so stupid?

The thought of jumping in the water crossed my mind again. I just didn't know if I could make myself take a breath. I wasn't sure that I could stay down there, and not try for the surface, but the quiet world below that green glassy window was beckoning.

I traced the small shape in my left front pocket. It was there, always there. The corkscrew on the small Swiss Army knife had become my new go-to. I hadn't used it in a while, so I'd probably have to work a little harder. There wasn't a cut or even a scab. I'd have to start a new one on top of the little scar. I'd sharpened the tip, but it never worked as well as my nail.

I sat down in my familiar spot. I scraped it across my tan skin. Once. Twice. Three times. It scratched the surface nicely. I pulled off a tiny little string of skin that the point had created. I repeated the process until the point got down to some nervier tissue. Wince. I pressed it harder. The air escaped through my clenched teeth. A little deeper.

I showed her. She kept me at home. She couldn't keep me from doing that. No one could. I could do that anytime I wanted. Anywhere I wanted. It felt good. My heart slowed as soon as the blood was visible.

Fuck them.

Fuck them all.

I walked back up to the house, had dinner, and laid in my bed until the moon was high in the sky and the oak limbs created shadows on my pillow case. I'd planned to stay up all night, just to spite them. All of them.

I didn't quite make it.

The obnoxious beep of the alarm clock startled me.

What? Fuck I fell asleep.

Saturday morning.

The green numbers on the loud little clock showed 7:30 A.M. I had to be at work by 8:00. The bile taste was still there on the back of my tongue. The anger from the day before still floating in front of me.

Fuck. My arm.

Soreness always set in the next day. Some days it hurt worse than others. I'd been mad when I cut it this time. I rolled right and eased my feet to the floor. No party. No beer. Somehow, I still felt hung over.

I unwrapped a BAND-AID and peeled off the little white paper. One side, and then the other. Mom probably wouldn't notice the small amount of blood on the sheets. After throwing on some wrinkled clothes, I drove mindlessly to work.

The usual Saturday morning shift. Eight until noon. We all rotated Saturdays, and Matt had this weekend off because of the party. The other guy was okay, but he wasn't Matt. It wasn't as fun when he wasn't around. Whatever. I would probably need to go in the freezer ten or fifteen times and maybe get some dried sausage or cheese out of the front case for a customer or two.

The freezer was my favorite. I worked deep, in the way back. The long lanes were narrow and tall, each containing ten shelves of meat, packed full from floor to ceiling. I worked at stacking the frozen white paper wrapped bricks of meat that had once been live cattle onto the little cart. I belted out "We Built This City" by Starship and danced to the sound of my own voice as I stacked. After the last packages were neatly arranged so they wouldn't fall off, I pushed the cart toward the front. The customer was out there waiting, probably reading a week-old copy of the paper or an outdated magazine from the bin next to the shitty green chair.

The handle boomed as I banged it outward with my back. The old coat I wore protected me from the blow. The big silver door swung open and slammed against the adjacent wall. The double-decker cart carrying the baskets I'd just stacked swerved on the little bits of ice that had just broken off the door seal when I'd opened it.

I began stuffing the frozen briquettes into the tall brown sacks while the customer watched. I marked each sack with the appropriate cuts – hamburger, steaks, roasts. When I glanced up, I noticed a couple of my friends out front through the big glass window. They seemed to be discussing something frantically, and one of them was jumping around like a cricket on a hot hood. I giggled and waved at them through the big front glass. They waved me out. In my best sign language, I explained that I would be out as soon as I finished up with the customer.

Once he'd paid, we both humped the awkward sacks out to his truck. I strategically placed the last one in the back seat and watched him drive away. As soon as I turned around, my friends walked over.

"Have you heard?" one of them asked.

"Heard what?"

"About the wreck," she replied.

"What wreck?"

"Simon crashed his car last night…"

"What?" I cut her off.

"Simon crashed his car last night with a couple other guys,"

"What do you mean crashed?" I asked. "Are they alright? Is Simon alright?"

"He's dead," she said flatly. "And the others are in the hospital."

"What? What the fuck?"

"It's true," someone else chimed in.

"Are you sure?" I asked desperately. "What others?"

They weren't sure. It was just the rumor around town. They were almost sure, but not positive.

"I'm not sure how it happened or who was in the car," she said. "But I'm pretty sure Simon is dead. No one would make that shit up."

"What?" I was confused. "Fuck. Fuck"

"They crashed coming down the hill from the party," she said. "He's dead."

But no one had confirmed it. Maybe it wasn't true.

Panic set in. I sprinted back in and looked at the clock. Fifteen minutes left.

"I gotta go. I gotta go." I told the coworker who wasn't Matt.

"Okay," he said.

"I gotta go," I muttered. "Simon might be dead."

My truck door swung open heavily. I jumped in and turned the key.

What the fuck?

There has to be a mistake.

A misunderstanding.

It has to be someone else.

Not sure where I was going, I slammed it in gear and spun out of the parking lot.

A small group was gathered in front of 7-11. The girls were crying. I parked by the outside gas pump and walked over.

I knew. I knew right then that the rumors were true.

"Watson…have you heard?" a buddy asked.

"Yep," I said.

No one said anything for what felt like a couple minutes. I felt completely numb. My mind refused to wrap around it.

"What happened?" I finally asked.

"Not sure," he replied.

"I was supposed to have been there. I was supposed to have been in the car with Simon," I said

Maybe I was supposed to be dead too?

Would they have crashed if I'd been there?

I might have been driving.

Simon would be alive.

We'd have taken my truck.

I'd have been with them at the party and we'd have left earlier or later or not at all and we wouldn't have crashed.

Confusion slipped in. It didn't make sense. I'd talked to him the day before. He couldn't be dead. He just couldn't.

But he was. My best friend died in April of 1985. He got drunk at a bachelor party and swerved off the road on his way back to town. He overreacted and swerved back across the road and into the opposite ditch.

His big white car hit the first culvert and catapulted into the air. From all accounts, it had flipped end over end at least three times. It eventually started barrel rolling and threw everyone out. No one had been wearing seat belts. All the other passengers survived. Simon did not. He was pronounced dead in the early hours of the morning.

The cassettes were there, in a little stack when I woke the next morning. They were blurry.

>*What the fuck?*
>
>*Why are all of my fucking cassettes in my room?*
>
>*Why were they on my floor?*
>
>*I'm on the floor.*
>
>*Where's the carpet?*
>
>*Fuck.*
>
>*Where am I?*

I lifted my head and immediately regretted it. I quickly laid it back down on the seat. Rolling to my side, I looked up, through the passenger side window. New growth was just beginning to burst from buds on the pecan tree. The long horizontal limbs swayed in a slight breeze. My feet were cold and numb.

>*Shoes. Where the hell are my shoes?*

I lifted my head again, this time making it up to the bottom of my dirty window. Mom's suburban was parked in the driveway. The sky was cloudy. I had no idea what time it was. I slid my hand down and felt outside the pocket of my acid-washed Levis.

Keys? Nope.

Of course. They were still in the ignition.

My hand hurt. I lifted it up and tried to focus. The bloody knuckles were stiff as I tried to work my fingers open and closed. Cuts. Deep cuts.

>*Holy shit.*

One of my fingers was swollen to twice its size. The skin was tight, and it wouldn't bend.

My head swam as I forced myself to sit upright. The Bud Light bottle opener keychain jangled as I tried the ignition.

The key finally turned half a turn to auxiliary, just enough to get the radio going. It was 6 am.

Birds sang and flitted around from the back of the house to the front, just as if I wasn't laying there. To them, everything seemed normal. They didn't know that I'd woken up in my truck. They didn't even seem to notice that my truck was on the front lawn.

My hands were a hamburger mess.

My head hurt and my mouth tasted like a cat had shit on my tongue.

I had no idea where I'd gone or what I'd done or who I'd fucked or how I'd gotten home or why I hadn't gone inside.

Inside. I needed to get inside.

The truck door creaked when it opened. My bare feet left tracks in the cold damp grass. I reached the front porch, managed the steps, and somehow chose the right key for the lock. The old shag carpet barely whispered as I slid my feet toward my room.

I collapsed and melted into my bed.

The house was quiet when I woke. I wasn't sure how long I'd been there or how long my eyes had been open. Sunlight spilled in through the half-closed curtains and seemed to warm the floor beside my bed. I couldn't move. I didn't want to move. I wanted to stay there forever. As I drifted in and out of a numb sleepy state, I tried to remember where I'd gone and what I'd done the night before.

Memories of Simon flickered in and out on the movie screen behind my eyes. It was like watching an old reel-to-reel. Flickers and flashes of camping trips and fishing and swimming in stock tanks and dipping snuff. All those nights by the camp fire. Whiskey drinks. Playboy centerfolds. Christmas mass. Eating Jesus' bread and drinking his wine.

I tried to imagine being in the car with them. Laughter and smiles as the wind blew in the open windows. Screams and fear as the car careened off the road and started its death rolls. Where would I have been sitting? Would I have been thrown out? Would I be alive? Or would all my hopes and dreams vanish in an instant, just like Simon's had.

One of the other guys was still in a coma. No one was sure if he'd make it. He didn't know about Simon yet.

I prayed for him to stay in his coma a while longer. Whatever dreams and fantasies he was living out underneath the blanket of his unconsciousness had to be better than the reality that awaited him on this side.

The screen door banged softly. Mom's shadow appeared in my doorway and didn't move.

"You okay?" she asked gently.

"Mmhmm," I replied.

"I tried to wake you for church," she said. "I got worried when I couldn't get you up."

"Sorry," I said.

"I even tried rolling you over," she kept talking. "Then I smelled alcohol and figured it was no use."

"Sorry,"

"It's okay," she said. "I know you're upset about Simon."

I really didn't want to talk about that. Not now. Not to her. Not to anyone.

Did she know I'd slept in my truck? Fuck. It was in the yard.

Did she think I was out all night and slept somewhere else? I had no idea. I didn't really care.

She was almost overly nice and soft. If she'd been mad and loud and mean it would have been easier. I deserved it.

She left it at that.

After she walked away, I finished the lecture she should have given me.

"Your friend just died in a drunken car wreck," I mouthed the words for her.

"It should have been a lesson to you," she should've said

"How could you disrespect Simon like that," I imagined her anger.

"How could you possibly let his death be in vain?"

"How could you go out the very next night and get drunk?"

"How could you get in your truck and drive home?"

"How could you...?"

"Why did you...?"

"Why are you...such a piece of shit?" I wanted to hear it from her mouth.

She would have been right and I knew it. Her imaginary words stung.

She never said them.

What a piece of shit.

THIRTY-TWO

The lid was locked down tight on the casket. The wreck had fucked him up
so badly they couldn't make him presentable enough for viewing. It really
pissed me off. I needed to see him one more time. I just wanted to look at
him and let him know how I felt. I stared through a blurry tunnel.
Everything was just out of focus. A few swigs of Jim Beam and a six-pack
of Bud Light had helped get me in the door. Now I wasn't so sure I was
going to be able to make it through the service.

And then…Simon. Smiling as big as ever. The framed eight-by-ten
of my friend was propped up there on that box. He'd never open it. No one
would ever open it. He'd be lying in there forever.

I swayed a little left, and then right as the long procession of people
eased forward.

I wish they'd hurry goddammit.

Everyone knew him. But not everyone had known him like me. It
struck me all at once. He'd been the best friend I'd ever had.

The jealousy caught me off guard. It welled up from nowhere and
wrapped around my throat. It strangled me. My spit turned to sand. I
couldn't breathe.

What are they even doing here?
Get the fuck out of here.
None of them really know him.
Not like I do.

Desperate. I'd never feel that closeness with anyone else.
Gone.

She sat in the front row, head down, sobbing. Her black shawl couldn't shield her from her own pain or the sorrow of the many people around her.

As if she sensed me getting close, she looked over her shoulder. I was about six people deep in the line. She stood up and waited for me to reach her. Her thin arms wrapped me up and I immediately felt the weight of her loss. His mother.

All selfish thoughts vanished. I held her up as we gently rocked back and forth.

"All that time," she kept repeating. "All that time."

We'd spent so much time out there at his house...their house. She'd seen us go through so much.

I wondered if she knew that I was supposed to have been in the car with them. Did she blame me for not being there and driving him home safely? Maybe she was glad I hadn't gone because I would be dead too. Could she smell the booze on my breath as I cried my tears on her shoulder?

THIRTY-THREE

It had only been a couple months since Simon's funeral. I'd thought about him every day. Every day.

One day, Sammy showed up. He slipped right in and filled the hole I'd felt in my chest after Simon died. He'd just walked up and sat down next to me at the Bar-B-Que joint. I was licking sauce off of my fingers and he pulled the chair out and had a seat.

"You going to the dance tonight?" he'd asked.

"Yep," I'd said.

He invited himself to ride with me. I didn't really know why. He was older, cooler, and already out of high school. None of that seemed to matter to him. We rode to that dance together. We'd ridden to every dance together since then.

The speakers pounded against my skull. That song. On the tip of my tongue. The cover band was doing a pretty good job, but I couldn't quite get the name to come to me. I snaked my way through the crowd of bobbing, swaying teenagers. Stale alcohol and cheap cologne assaulted my nose.

Where is she?

Who is she?

I had no idea who I was looking for, but I'd know her when I saw her. She just had to be drunk enough. Or sober and willing to come home with me.

I kept looking. She'd be standing alone or dancing with other girls, or maybe joining in as a third with another couple. She might even be dancing with a boyfriend who didn't intimidate me. We'd make eye contact and seal the deal before speaking a word. She'd know it. I'd know it. We'd be leaving together. It always happened that way.

The dried leaves of giant live oaks crackled beneath my shoes as I walked in the general direction of the location I thought I'd parked the truck. Neither of us was actually sober enough to drive, but I'd won the coin toss. Sammy would somehow have to get us back safely.

Try as we had, neither of us left this dance with a girl. It was a little unusual but no big deal. The night was still young.

We pulled into Smithville and circled back around to the Kwik Pantry. We'd scoped out two girls driving into the parking lot and they didn't appear to have guys with them. We sat. We watched. The AC circulated the cherry smell from the little air freshener on the vent. The girls simultaneously got out of a dirty little blue car, one from the driver's side and one from the other.

A humid south wind blew their hair up and around. The one in the lead stumbled on the parking curb as they half walked, and half ran into the store. Sammy looked over at me.

"Which one you want?" he asked.

They looked almost like twins – tall, blond, tight jeans, baggy sweaters.

"Doesn't matter."

He pointed at the car door.

"Go for it," he said. There was a slight challenge in his tone.

"You sure?"

"Pick one," he said. "Do your thing."

"Okay. But you can pick first if you want."

"I gotta 12-pack that says you can't get her in the car right now," he said.

His fake smile was all the motivation I needed.

"Hold my beer. This'll be easy."

My insides stayed inside as I opened the door and met them on their way out of the store. I twisted the top off of a fresh beer as I walked slowly and deliberately, right toward them. The smell of fried chicken gizzards and french fries wafted out of the little building. The six pack of wine coolers they'd just bought jingled as the girl in the lead made sure not to trip on the curb again. We all stopped at the same time, about halfway between the store and their car.

I walked tall and straight. No bees. No sweat. I'd had just enough to drink. And this was my game.

They were both in the car within five minutes.

Sammy cranked up White Snake's "Slide it In" and looked over at me with a shit-eating grin. His girl reached over and placed her hand on his as he shifted into Drive. Mine was already straddling me in the back seat. She was going to be number ten. Or was it eleven?

The tornado that lived inside me was silent. My new best friend was awesome.

We got drunk.

We had fun.

Sex seemed easy.

I felt normal.

THIRTY-FOUR

I walked into the party. The two beers stacked in my right hand were cold…fresh from the cooler. It was becoming my trademark, at least in my own mind. My Panama Jack Koozie held the lower unopened beer and the open one was stacked on top. I always felt like I needed two.

I scanned the room as I finished the top beer. Removing the bottom one from the Koozie, I promoted it to the top and shoved a fresh cold one down in its spot. Two felt like the number of beers I should carry around. So, I did.

She was standing over by the keg. The music was loud. Survivor belted out "The Search is Over" as I swaggered toward her. She was the same girl Sammy and I had made the bet on at the gas station a few weeks before.

I'd had sex with her that night.

In the back seat.

While Sammy had driven around town.

It had been one of my usual drunk nights – few memories, a lot of hangover.

"Hey. I haven't seen you in a while," I said.

"Oh, so you remember me?" she asked flatly.

"Of course," I said. "How could I forget you…or that night."

"You were supposed to call."

"I…I lost your number?" We both laughed.

Luckily she carried the conversation. She giggled and reminded me about some details of our drunken escapade. I knew by the way she locked eyes with me that we were headed for another.

I was buzzing pretty good, but not drunk. For some reason, a little bit of panic crawled up and through my body. A tingly feeling flowed from my feet and up through my legs. It washed across my crotch and stopped in my stomach. The tingle turned to sparks and I suddenly needed another beer.

She was drunk. She looked really, really good. I was up to about fifteen girls at that point, and usually felt pretty confident during this part of the deal. I wasn't sure where this nervous energy was coming from, but I just kept feeling like I needed another beer. And then another.

I drank them as we talked.

She suddenly turned and brushed her lips against mine.

"You wanna get out of here?" she asked. Her breathy whisper tickled the hair on my neck.

"Sounds good," I said.

We said a couple goodbyes and jumped into her shitty little blue car.

"You okay to drive?" she asked.

"You bet," I said. I'd just automatically jumped behind the wheel. "Hand me another beer."

The car sputtered and jumped as we left the party and sped down the winding road.

"Left here," she said a little too loudly. She'd been kissing my neck and running her hand along the inside of my leg.

"Shit."

I swerved off the highway and made a quick stop in her driveway. The beer in my lap ended up on the floor.

Nerves.

I felt myself heating up. The warmth made its way up from under my shirt and into my face. I knew I was turning red and I knew she saw it. The sweat would be next.

I'd had quite a few beers at the party and three on the road to her place but wasn't quite drunk. I was always drunk during a hookup. And, I usually didn't hook up with anyone twice. I could never get the courage to call them back after they'd given me their number.

I liked her. She liked me. I thought she did. She was pretty drunk. *What the fuck?*

Before I could get the door open she slid her head down in my lap. There was no way out now.

She came up for a breath.

"You wanna go inside?" she asked. "I can't fuck you in this car."

"Sure," I said.

The look in her eyes unnerved me. She laughed as she squeezed me in her hand.

I walked around and opened her door. She poured out of the car like warm honey. She was limp and limber and couldn't have walked a straight line if her life had depended on it.

"The house key is next to the car key," she said.

There were a lot of keys. The house key was actually not next to the car key. It didn't seem to be next to any key. The pink fuzzy troll key-chain thingy watched as I jingled and jangled at the lock.

"Don't worry. My parents aren't home," she said.

"I'm not worried," I said.

But I was. Not about her parents, but about the ball of spinning energy I was feeling in the pit of my stomach. I just couldn't quite find that perfect drunk.

I finally found the right key and turned the knob. Stall. I had to stall.

The barrage of thoughts came at me.

Shut up.

Calm down.

You can do this.

What's wrong with you?

She's right there.

But deep down I didn't believe I could do it.

Something clicked as we were getting into the heavy breathing and rubbing. She grabbed my left hand and slid it up to her boobs. I quickly slid it back to her stomach. She tried again. This time I left it there.

She half sat up and slid her t-shirt over her head. She unbuttoned her jeans and laid back on the little bed.

Holy shit.

This is it.

What the fuck? Why is this different?

She put my hands back on her. I could only see her forearm as she

167

rubbed herself inside her jeans.

She violently pulled me down on top of her. Kissing. Touching. Raking her fingernails across the back of my shirt.

Then she thrust upward and flipped me over beside her. She was down on me before I could ask her why the fuck she did that.

"What's wrong?" she asked.

"Nothing," I said.

"Are you sure?" she sounded worried.

"Where's the bathroom?" I asked.

"I don't know," she said.

"What?" I asked. "Isn't this your fucking house?"

"Yeah," she slurred.

"I'm gonna go piss," I said.

She didn't answer.

I stumbled over some shoes and clutched at a fake plant as I fell across the entry-way. The little yellow bathroom lit up as I flipped on the light switch. Somehow, I'd randomly picked the right hall and pretty much landed on the toilet as I stumbled through the doorway. I really had to pee.

I puked instead.

I peed.

I puked again.

The handle squeaked when I turned the water on. I rinsed my mouth out with lukewarm water. The sink was dirty. I picked up the hand-towel and almost wiped my mouth on it. It looked as if it hadn't been washed in at least a week. I changed my mind, used the back of my hand, and turned off the light.

The hall was dark but straight. My hand rubbed against the rough paint as I walked.

What am I going to do? She really wants to fuck.

I peeked into the room.

Relief washed over me. Her eyes were closed. Her long black lashes seemed to reach half way down her cheeks. Her naked chest moved up and down with each easy, rhythmic breath. I tiptoed in and grabbed the shoes I'd tossed in the corner. One more glance.

She was completely naked. No clothes. No covers. I could do anything I wanted to her. Creamy tan skin. Oversized pouty lips. What to do?

I puked on the carpet.

Her keys were on the little table in the hallway. I grabbed them and slipped out.

A tinny little noise came from under the hood when I cranked the ignition.

Fuck. What if it doesn't start?

Fucking piece of shit.

After thumping the steering wheel three or four times, it finally cranked. I took her shitty little blue car back out onto the highway and retraced our route back to the party.

"Watson," a buddy yelled across the room when I walked back in to the house party.

"Hell yeah." I yelled back.

"Dude," he said. "That was quick."

"No shit," I said.

"What the fuck?" he asked.

"She passed out before I could get down to it," I lied.

"Well there's plenty of beer left," he said. "Let's grab a couple and hit the road."

I left her keys on the coffee table by the front door on my way out.

As I sat there in the back seat of my buddy's car I tried to quell my feelings of shame, and even guilt, for not fucking her. I hadn't been able to make myself do what I knew anyone else would have. The feeling was familiar.

The guilt caught me off guard. The guilt was for her. She'd wanted me. She'd laid herself out for me. Completely exposed herself. She'd been one-hundred percent confident that if she took those clothes off and let me have that body, I'd take it. I'd have appreciated it.

I hadn't done either. All I'd done was let her down. I was overwhelmed.

I tried to laugh it off.

"Turn up the fucking radio," I said.

As I leaned over the middle console and stuck my head forward, a bottle of Jim Beam was staring me in the face.

One giant swig. And then a second...

He drove fast and loud. I looked around each corner for something to make me feel better.

Instead, I found the nearest blackout. I found it within the hour.

The next morning felt different. Even though I'd woken up in my truck again with the birds and other familiar sounds, something was off. Something had shifted inside me. I thought about the previous night.

Failure. The realization that I couldn't really function on any level without being buzzed overwhelmed me. My mind spun wildly.

What the fuck is wrong with me?

Just thinking about it made me feel caged and angry. Like one of those animals at the zoo that constantly paces up and down the fence-line, back and forth, looking for something. Never quite knowing what. But looking for something.

When I had a few beers in me everything was different. The pacing stopped. The tornado in my head slowed. The cage doors opened. I felt normal. I was funny. I could carry on a conversation without sweating. I could have sex.

I wondered why no one around me seemed to feel this way. Everything I did or tried to do seemed so complicated. Why couldn't I function like my friends without being smashed? My thoughts always seemed to be fucking up a good thing?

For a while it all seemed simple…I'd get drunk and I'd feel good. I'd get drunk and have sex with anyone who happened to be there.

She'd been right there, naked, horny, hot.

I'd failed.

Now what?

THIRTY-FIVE

Sammy flashed his high-beams at me on the loop and I pulled around the back side of the block.

"What's up?" I asked.

"You got beer?" he asked right back.

"A few in the cooler," I said.

"Pick me up at the KP," he said.

My mood picked up as I made the corner and pulled back onto the main drag. The smell of fried onion rings made my mouth water as I rolled by the Burger Joint. I'd just been riding up and down the strip by myself. Shitty feelings mixed with shitty music from the local radio station. Nothing much in mind. Searching for something. Not sure what.

He was waiting when I pulled in the parking lot behind the little store.

"Grab me another one," I said when I heard him pop open the cooler lid.

"Hell yeah." He handed me two.

We made the loop over and over. The cold beer went down easy. My melancholy lifted for good when Billy Squire's high-pitched voice pierced the hum drum conversation we were having. We both stopped talking and belted our own twangy duo version of "The Stroke". It was one of our favorites and we'd sung it together a hundred times.

He banged his head back and forth as he sang. His left fist was clenched and pumped the air. Then he pulled out the little baggy.

"What's that?" I asked.

"Your birthday party is about to start," he said.

"What?"

I wasn't planning on a celebration. Seventeen seemed like just another year. Kind of boring. I got my driver's license at fifteen. I'd be an adult at eighteen. Seventeen…blah.

"I just figured we'd get drunk." I smiled.

His teeth looked oversized as he gnashed them together in a crazy clenched smile.

"This shit'll give you energy to party all night," he said.

"Okay…what the hell." I replied. One small second of hesitancy was overrun by the beer in my brain.

"And, we can drink for hours and not get drunk," he added.

"What the fuck is the point of drinking if we can't get drunk?" I asked with a laugh.

"That's not what I mean," he said. "We can drink and get drunk…but not pass-out drunk."

"Oooooh. Well in that case…Fucking A," I yelled.

He pinched at the top of the little clear bag and finally pulled the sides apart. He reached in, grabbed one of the tiny white pills and handed it to me. I popped it in my mouth as I shifted from second to third gear, having just made the turn at the west end of the loop. I held the small white pill in my mouth for a few seconds until the bitter taste found the back of my tongue. I chased it down with half of a beer and smiled over at Sammy. He gave me another clenched smile and then popped the one he'd gotten for himself. His eyes were the size of silver dollars. His jaw muscles stuck out more than usual due to the pressure he was exerting with his bite.

"What the fuck are you doing?" I asked. He didn't seem like his usual self.

"You'll see," he said.

We rode a few more loops and drank a few more beers.

We each popped one more pill. Sammy smiled like a wooden puppet with oversized square teeth. We were both wide-eyed and seemed to be trying to out smile each other. My clenched smile competing with his. I stopped when my jaw muscles started to cramp and a rush of heat and pressure made my eyes bulge.

The thunderous pounding of my pulse in my ears drowned out everything else. I could hear the radio. Sammy's lips were moving. But I could only hear the thump thumping of my rapid heartbeat.

My chest was going to explode at any moment. It had to. There was an invisible belt around my middle and someone was cinching it up...tighter and tighter.

What the fuck?

My breath was coming faster and faster...as if I was running a race. But I was sitting still. My only exertion, clenching...smiling.

My fingers tingled and the hair on my arms stuck straight out. When I clenched my teeth together again, I couldn't feel them.

Goddamit.

My eyes were wide open – stuck that way. I tried to close them, but they kept popping open. Wider and wider. I opened my mouth to relax my jaw, but it immediately closed again and clenched tight.

"Something's wrong," I said. "Something's fucking wrong."

"Chill dude,' he said. "Just head for the river bridge."

"What the fuck?" I asked. "Why are we going down there?"

"I gotta fucking pee," he said. "And we can assess the situation."

The truck double hopped as I made the corner and didn't quite clear the hump on the side of the road. I fish-tailed left and then right, finally coming to a partial stop.

The truck was still rolling when my feet hit the ground. As it slowly stopped in the soft sand, I was already pacing around from front to back. Front to back. Front to back. My chest was definitely going to explode. This was definitely a heart attack.

"What the fuck, man?" I yelled. "What the fuck?"

Sammy grabbed me by the shoulders and looked into my eyes. Spinning me around, we began walking around the truck. First one way. Then the other. Around and around. He kept his hand on my right shoulder.

"Just chill," he said. "Just chill."

His voice was a sort of loud whisper.

"Just chill man," He said it over and over and we kept walking. Circling.

Suddenly there was mud under my feet. Wind blowing over my skin. The sound of crickets bounced around the inside of my skull. The river was rushing by just below us and the rumbling sound of cars going over the bridge sounded like intermittent drum beats. Blump, blump,

blump, blump…one car. Blump, blump, blump, blump…another.

I heard myself yell again.

"What the fuck, man? What the fuck?"

This time I was above my body looking down. We kept circling. His face showed panic as if he was making life or death decisions in his head.

"Take you to the hospital and admit giving you the shit?" he was talking to me, but not.

"Just drop you off at the ER door?" he asked me, sort of.

"Take you home and tell your parents?"

He was talking but his words weren't aimed in my direction. As if he were just weighing all the options in his head. They were coming out as words through his clenched teeth.

"Take you home and drop you off on the front porch?" he assessed another possibility.

"No. Fuck no," he said. This time he wasn't whispering.

The rhythm of my heart. Loud. Fast. Regular.

There was no short pause between beats, just a constant thump, thump, thump. The jumping muscle felt as if it was touching the inside of my chest. It was bouncing off my ribs and contracting faster and faster and faster.

Suddenly, my vision wouldn't focus on anything. The scene in front of me appeared as if in a painting.

"Where the fuck are we," I heard myself ask.

I looked for landmarks but could only see the painting. I searched for details.

"Chill man, just chill," he said.

He held me up when I tried to sit.

"Keep walking man," he said. "Just keep walking.

We kept walking. Laps and laps around the truck. Then, to the paved road and back. All the way over to a big sycamore tree. Around the tree. Again. Again. Maybe a hundred times.

"Where the fuck are we?" I asked again.

"Under the river bridge," he said.

It didn't make any sense. My view was scrambled and still out of focus.

We made the corner, around the back of the truck for the

thousandth time. Suddenly, everything changed.

Just as my eyes and brain were trying to remedy the picture in front of me... Swoooooooooosssshhhhhh.

The painting suddenly went from wide angle, large view, non-detailed, to close-up, small view, super focused. Each jagged grain of sand that made up each tiny droplet of mud on the left rear fender. Every tiny sun baked crack in the KLBJ window sticker on the back window of the truck. Individual veins in the leaves of the Johnson grass plant we'd crushed as we were parking the truck. And suddenly...Sammy.

Fear vibrated through his voice. He moaned deeply and in slow motion, as if he were tranquilized. He repeated what he'd been saying all along.

"Just chill."

"Keep walking."

"Just chill."

"Keep walking."

And so I did.

We walked.

He talked.

He walked me around the truck a hundred more times.

"It's just me and you man," he said. I'd never heard that kind of emotion in his voice.

"Yeah," I replied.

"We can only count on each other," he said.

"I know," I replied.

"Nobody else is gonna help us," he said. "We gotta stick together."

We talked about the girls we'd been with. He talked about his family. We talked about our friends. We talked about the little white pills we'd taken that night.

"After the pills we were supposed to hook up with those girls from earlier," he said.

I listened.

"X can make you Superman."

"You can stay up all night."

"You can drink all night."

"You can fuck all night."

We walked.

We talked.

One minute we were walking and talking in the dark. The faint light of the moon and a couple of street lights on the bridge overhead helped us see the truck and each other. I only blinked.

Daylight. We were still walking around the truck. The sun was out. A yellow and black Swallow-tail butterfly floated around us, up and over the truck, and wafted away with the breeze.

"It's just me and you man. Just me and you."

"I know," I replied. "We gotta stick together."

THIRTY-SIX

"Dude give me another one," I said.

"You already had two," Sammy replied.

"So fucking what?"

"You almost had a heart attack a couple weeks ago."

"Oh yeah."

"I don't wanna be walking you around the fucking truck all night."

We looked at each other and laughed. Our high-five slapped and we both turned our beers up and guzzled them down. The Miller Lite soothed my throat. It was icy and straight out of the cooler. We'd been riding around town for a couple of hours and we'd already gone through a case. Twelve each, give or take. And still, I couldn't get rid of the sand on my tongue. Dry. Parched. It was the only drawback I'd discovered with the Ecstasy.

Other than that, I was superhuman. Invincible. Focused. Buzzed. An unfamiliar happiness was settling in on me. The smile on my face wasn't forced. The laugh from my chest was genuine.

Sammy ran into the 7-11 to pay for the eight dollars of gas he'd just pumped and grab some beer. That was all that remained of our combined cash.

I scraped the cassettes into a pile on the seat. They rattled as I scooped them up and threw them on the dash among the others, some already sun-warped. It really wasn't the best place to put them.

The girls were just tumbling out of their car and about to hop in with us. Sammy held up a fresh 12-pack and smiled when he saw them. He hopped in the driver's seat and the girls slid over me and settled into the middle. The beer can let out a familiar *swish...pop*. He cranked up Def Leppard "Action! Not Words" and punched the gas pedal to the floor. The tires squawked as we made the corner out of the pot-holey parking lot.

My long hair flew wildly as the wind from the passenger window crossed through the truck. The music blasted through the six-by-nines and vibrated my back through the seat. Golden-brown legs emerged from the cutoffs next to me. Super short cutoffs and tank tops. The too-fast beat of my heart was in sync with the music. Superman pills had sped my pulse from a normal rhythmic thump to an all-out rock and roll assault.

A quick side-eyed assessment confirmed what I first thought when I saw them. These girls would be easy. They were already laughing and head banging to the music. They'd driven over from Bastrop, the next town west, along Highway 71. They looked kind of familiar but I wasn't sure of names. I thought I'd seen them around at parties and riding up and down the highway after midnight.

It didn't matter. I didn't really care if they had names. They may or may not have been looking for the same thing we were. But that's all they were going to get. A few beers and a quick fuck. If they expected more, they'd be sorely disappointed.

Sammy looked over at me and smiled a jaw-clenching smile. I returned the gesture. The girls were trying their best to sing along with the song. Neither of them knew the words.

I was finally feeling buzzed. Just drunk enough.

The streetlights disappeared. I strained my eyes to see past the beams of the truck's headlights. We were headed out of town. Sammy's girl was whispering something in his ear as he tried to keep his eyes on the road. The truck lunged forward as he floored the gas pedal and we sped into the darkness.

I slid over on top of the girl next to me when Sammy made the hard right. We all kind of slid toward the driver's side. The truck left the pavement and we were suddenly on a two-track gravel road.

One tiny square of light appeared way out in front of us and to the right. It grew larger as we got closer. The house only came into view when we pulled into the driveway. The orange light shined in patterns through a leathery looking lamp shade.

"I guess y'all left that lamp on so you could find this fucking house?" I asked with a smile. "Whose house is this anyway?"

"Mine," the girl next to Sammy chimed in. "My parents are out of town."

We all piled out at the same time and walked toward the house. It was dark. Really dark. I walked slowly, trying not to trip.

We slipped in through an unlocked side door. The kitchen was big and clean. I swung the fridge door wide and grabbed a beer. Sizing up my date for the night brought a smile to my face.

She was there. She was giggling drunk. That was enough. We hadn't even had to work for these two. They'd just driven up and jumped in with us.

She yanked my hand and we stumbled toward another part of the house. Beer sloshed from the top of my can as we kiss-walked sideways down the hall.

We rounded another corner and fell on top of each other. Her pink lacy bra was all I could focus on. My back pressed against the cold hardwood floor. Lamp table. Chair. Bed.

I kissed the warm sweet cherry lip-balm from her lips.

We finally made our way up to the bed in the corner of the room. She reached behind her back and unhooked her bra. She exploded from underneath it. I fell back on the floor.

Holy shit!

She jumped off the bed and straddled me. We fumbled and laughed and fumbled some more. And then we were both naked.

The X pulsed through my veins.

No slow start. No talking. No foreplay. We just got right down to it.

The house was quiet. She was loud. Her moans echoed down the hallway and back.

It was fast. Desperate.

I gritted my teeth as I looked down at her. I was proving my worth with each stroke.

Clawing.

Moaning.

Moving.

After what seemed like an hour, Sammy and his girl were suddenly murmuring in another room. We didn't stop. We only slowed down for a second or two to listen. We found each other's rhythm again and kept going.

The X was in full effect and I wasn't slowing down anytime soon. I could go all night. I was in tune with everything.

Every drop of cool sweat.

Every note of her raspy moaning voice. I consumed every ounce of her energy as she directed it toward my body.

"Dude," Sammy said from the other room.

Silence.

"Dude."

What the fuck? Is he crazy?

'If you wanna fucking ride back to the Ville, you'd better hurry up," he said

"Don't go," she begged.

The keys jingled. I didn't want to hear him. I wanted to stay right where I was and keep doing what I was doing.

Even though I barely knew this girl I felt somehow connected to her. We felt entwined. Not just physically, but spiritually. I didn't know why. Like we'd suddenly realized we'd known each other forever. Maybe it was the X.

"Don't go," she said again.

The skin on my upper back tingled as she scraped gently with her nails.

What the fuck?

What the fuck is her name?

I suddenly snapped out of the weird spell I was under. I knew I didn't want to be left stranded there with a strange girl who I'd just met...and fucked. I didn't want to depend on her to give me a ride home or to endure that thirty minutes of silence. So, I focused. I really focused. I wanted to finish. I had to finish.

I narrowed my vision and my thoughts to what we were doing.

Nothing.

I focused on the motion. The back and forth motion.

Nope.

Come on...I can do this.

I couldn't. I couldn't make it happen. She'd already had hers...twice, maybe three times. But, try as I might I couldn't close the deal.

I could've gone on forever. I was nowhere near done. I hadn't even started getting those warning tremors. Those little shots of electricity way down inside, letting me know I was close.

Nothing.

Fuck.

I suddenly jumped off of her and grabbed my pants. Sammy had already started the truck and I wasn't sure I'd be able to catch him before he left me. I turned back at the door.

"I'll call you," I said with my brightest smile.

"Sure," she said sarcastically. "I'll wait on that."

We both laughed. There was always a chance we'd hook up again...but it would be just like this time. Drunk. Right place. Right time.

I jumped in just as Sammy was slamming my four-speed into gear. He smiled. Another minute, he'd have left me.

"Dude," he said. "I figured you were in it for the long one."

"Me too, motherfucker," I said. I was slightly pissed.

"How'd those two Xs work out for ya?" he asked with a chuckle.

"Well..."

"I heard you man," he said. "Sounded like they were working fine."

"Why'd you fucking cut me off?" I tried my best to hide the anger.

He just ignored me and fumbled with the radio.

He laughed when I told him I told her I was going to call. We'd both been in awkward situations before. That moment-after-sex conversation. Those weird looks and fleeting words.

No thanks.

Sammy punched it and Frankie Goes to Hollywood sang "Relax Don't Do It" as we swerved sideways out of the gravel driveway and into the street. My anger faded as the mud-grips squealed and caught traction on the asphalt. We were off again. Just the two of us. Into the night. Off to who knows where to find who knows what with who knows who.

More beer.

More X.

More girls. For sure.

THIRTY-SEVEN

My glazed eyes scanned the empty steer pen. Z-Bo sniffed the fence corners and under the unused shed. I'd opened the backyard gate and let him out into the larger enclosure before driving my truck back and parking in the shade.

He was only a pup when I'd gotten him from a friend. I kept him in Grandma's back yard, and she fed and watered him for me. Since he was a pit bull, she called him her guard dog. He mostly got excited about riding the drag and swimming in the river, but Grandma felt safer having him around.

The mirror snagged on a loose corner of my floor mat, but finally slid from under the seat with a little jiggling. A light dusty film had settled on it since last week. My hand was shaking as I opened the tiny zippy.

How do they make Ziplocs that small?

Part of the powder had started sticking to the sides...my upper lip began to bead with sweat. I rubbed my thin blond fuzz mustache against my shoulder and dumped the clumpy tan/brown powder out on the small glass. I angled it away slightly so I couldn't see my face while I chopped at the little rocks with the blade. I'd lost my only razor blade, so I was using my pocket knife.

I'd only done crank a couple times before. I needed more. I'd used X a bunch since that first time with Sammy months before. But mostly when I knew I was going to hook up with someone. If there wasn't a chick in the plans for the night or if I didn't find one along the way, I'd usually save it.

I'd tried Coke a couple times, but the high wore off in an hour and it was too expensive. Crank wasn't cheap either, but a few hits lasted all night. A buddy had given me the little baggy the day before for giving him a ride out to his house in the country.

I'd been drunk all those other times. This was the first time without a few beers in my system.

I was sober.

I felt like shit.

Mom and Dad were pissed again. I'd crashed my truck into some trees the night before and slightly caved the hood in. It wasn't as bad as some of my other wrecks, but they'd become a little too regular for my parents.

I knew I disappointed them. They'd asked me to slow down. They'd asked me to stop. They only knew about the drinking.

They didn't need to try and guilt me into not staying out so late. Not drinking so much. Not driving when I could barely walk. Guilt and shame had cornered the market on my thoughts and feelings. I didn't want to keep letting them down.

I wished I could tell them.

There always seemed to be something I wished I could tell them.

I'd cut myself a couple of times during the week. Same routine as always, but with minimal result. The crazy tornado in my head just wouldn't slow down. Thoughts swirled and screamed and crashed into one another. It had become nonstop.

The clump of powder waited there on the mirror. I tried not to spill it or accidentally blow it off with my heavy breathing.

Shaking.

Fuck. Maybe I should've drank a beer or two.

My nerves were frazzled.

Z-Bo had gone back up to his yard and left the big pen empty. It felt strange.

Zeke the steer was long gone.

I'd fed him.

I'd walked him.

He'd arched his back during every sudsy bath. He'd listened to my problems without complaint. But when the livestock show was over, he'd failed to make the top ten. So, Dad had traded him to my uncle.

"We'll eat your cousin's steer and they can eat yours," he'd said.

I'd cried at the thought of them eating him even though I'd always known that's what would eventually happen to him. I'd cried even more after finding out that the trade was a ruse.

There was no trade.

We'd actually eaten Zeke ourselves.

I'd eaten my friend.

Those motherfuckers.

The driver's side window was half-open and I could hear the harmony of the crickets letting me know that the day was almost done. I'd soon be in my element.

I looked up and down nervously as I re-chopped and re-lined the sticky powder. I couldn't get it to line out very good because it had gotten too hot and was trying to turn back into a liquid. I scraped at the gooey chunky lines, one to the left, one to the right. Back and forth with the shitty knife blade.

I eased my head down, placed one end of the red Dairy Queen straw to my right nostril, closed the left with my thumb…and sucked. I sucked as hard and long as I could…right line first, then left. I didn't even change nostrils.

Holy Fuck.

It burned so bad. No alcohol in my system and…it burned.

Tears came immediately. Big watery tears. Not crying tears. Big juicy, burning crank tears.

My sinuses were on fire.

I tasted the bitter numbness as it ran down the back of my throat. Through my sinuses. Into the back of my mouth. My eyes watered and I couldn't see if I'd gotten it all. It had only been a quarter-bag so there were only the two lines. Enough to burn the fuck out of my entire respiratory system and hopefully keep me wired for a long time.

More drainage. A little more burning. My throat and mouth were getting numb. Then it hit my empty stomach.

Fuck.

I heaved.

Whoa.

I had to hold it down. I knew I wouldn't get another freebie and I didn't have the twenty bucks I'd need to get more. My stomach hadn't flipped like this before. But I also hadn't done a whole quarter-bag without drinking before.

I stepped out of my truck and into the knee-high grass next to the path. My left foot found the top of the tire and I swung-jumped into the bed of the truck. The cooler lid squawked as I opened it. I stabbed my hand into the icy water and grabbed two beers. The first one went down smoothly, right there.

My whistle pierced the air and Z-Bo streaked out of the yard and over to the fence. He jumped up and hooked his front legs over the top, stuck his back feet in the chain links, about mid-way up, gave a little bounce and landed on my side. The tailgate was down and he was in the back of the truck with me in a second.

I jumped down, closed the tailgate and popped the second beer. Cold sticky foam slid down my hand and into my lap. The truck engine came to life as the door slammed behind me.

I cranked up AC/DC "Touch Too Much" and spun mud out behind me as I headed for town. The shitty feelings I'd had all over me just moments before were starting to melt away.

My stomach settled.

The rambling, rolling, swirling river of thoughts that always bombarded me were slowing to an ebb. Focused. Energetic. Calm.

Fuck yeah.

I slammed it in third, chugged the rest of the second beer and threw the can out the back of the sliding glass window. It barely missed Z-Bo, before rattling and clanging around a bit, and settling into place next to the pile of empty comrades. I Just drove. No destination in mind. I was feeling normal again.

THIRTY-EIGHT

I was nervous but couldn't quite put my finger on why. We sat around on the edge of the small bleachers, near the high jump pit. The spongy black track around the football field was newly laid and the bleachers were newly painted. A strong asphalt and paint smell from the new facilities hung around us.

My buddy Blake was dating a freshman and I was staring at her friend, Lynn. I was trying to find something to distract me and keep me from looking directly at her. I couldn't. Our eyes met every few seconds and she looked down when I stared too long.

She was fantastic. Her skin was tan, but not too tan. Just a hint of sunburn warmed her perfect cheeks. Her hair hung straight in the back and was kind of messed up in the front from cheerleading tryouts. She'd obviously put some work into it that morning. She battled one wispy strand, tucking it behind her ear again and again. She seemed annoyed. It was cute.

"Got any more of that gum?" I asked. I could barely hear my own words.

"Sorry," she said. "This is my last piece."

"Can I have it?" I asked.

"Are you crazy?" she asked. She laughed.

I was half joking, but secretly hoping she'd lean over and give me the gum with a big kiss.

She did not.

She looked directly into my eyes, spit it out into her hand, reached over, and popped it in my mouth. She was bold.

Holy shit…I was in love.

That weekend, Blake arranged for us all to drive over to a neighboring town and go bowling. I was a shitty bowler, but it was my first chance to hang out with Lynn since the day of the gum incident.

I'd seen her around school and knew that she was fresh out of a middle school relationship. She'd been dating someone from eighth-grade through the beginning of freshman year. Now that she was in high school, she was ready to move on, I guessed. I was a senior and that's how it had been for us as freshman, too—all the girls in our grade decided to trade up as soon as we hit freshman year. It had annoyed the hell out of us. But now I got it.

Freshman girls were, well, fresh. They hadn't been around the high school block. They had a kind of attractive innocence. I'd known most of the girls in my grade since kindergarten. Lynn was something new. She was an unknown.

I was a young senior, at seventeen, and was super intimidated by older girls. Ever since my drunk failed experience with the older girl my freshman year, I'd felt uncomfortable with girls who may have known too much…unless I was drunk. I wondered if all guys felt that way? Maybe that's why seniors liked freshmen.

We sat in the back seat of my Grandma's car. I twirled my index finger, making circles beside my leg on the grey plush seat. Another drunk wreck the weekend before had my truck back in for repairs. I'd been driving too fast again and didn't quite make a turn on my way home from a bonfire with Sammy. I'd been totally smashed. My truck went through a barbed-wire fence and ended up in a field. Dad and I had silently hauled it over to Shamrock's Paint and Body Shop. They'd seen a lot of my parent's money. A lot.

Blake drove the car and his girl sat in the middle of the bench seat, snuggled in under his arm. Lynn and I talked about how shitty we'd bowled. We talked about how cold it was outside. We talked about everything except what I really wanted to talk about. I wasn't drunk. My palms were starting to moisten up. I hoped she wouldn't notice.

I tucked my hands under my legs.

The bees and birds in my stomach were coming to life. At first, they buzzed lightly. When I started getting close to the question that was stuck in the back of my throat, they buzzed and flapped and spun. They started down low and moved upward in circles until they reached my chest. They all got lodged in my throat.

Fuck. What's wrong with me?

Blake's slow monotone voice seemed to lull his girl into a trance. The more he talked, the closer she skootched next to him. It looked effortless. He smiled and laughed and cracked great jokes.

I just sounded stupid. I talked about stupid shit. I was stupid.

Lynn looked over and our lips were suddenly pressing against each other's. It surprised me as much as her. The buildup. The electric motor in my gut. It had been too much. I'd planned to ask her out on an official date. But this was good.

We didn't talk.

We kissed.

Her innocence was there. Subtle. Sweet. I didn't try anything else. We just kissed while Blake drove.

We were still kissing when I looked up and noticed that we were back in Smithville.

"What do ya think, Watson?" Blake asked.

"Not sure," I said.

"When's your curfew?" I asked Lynn.

"Not really a curfew," she replied. "I'm just supposed to come home after bowling."

"Really?" I asked.

"Well," she said, kind of embarrassed. "Usually eleven o'clock."

"Fuck. Really?" I asked. "That's pretty early."

"Yep."

We decided we'd ride around town for a while before taking her home.

My chest loosened. My stomach was calm. Somewhere during the kissing, my bees and birds had stopped their shit.

We started talking again and I didn't feel nervous. We talked about our friends. We talked about people we had dated. She told me about her recent relationship and I told her about wrecking my truck. She wasn't fazed.

"You wanna go out again?" I finally got around to it.

"Sure," she said.

"But, will you go with me?" I asked. "Like, be my girlfriend go with me?"

"Yeah," she said smiling. "I thought that's what you meant."

Dad always got a kick out of that.

"Where you going?" he'd ask. Then he'd laugh his ass off. He knew full well that "go with me" meant "be my girlfriend".

So, there it was. I had a girlfriend. A real girlfriend. I'd dated a couple of girls in the few months before I'd met her, but they were only hookup girlfriends. The kind of girl you fuck first and then start dating. This was different. She was different. Genuine. Confident. As if she didn't need anything from me...she was fine just being her.

We kissed some more.

"I gotta get home," she said.

"Really?" I asked. I already knew her answer.

"I don't want to," she sounded sincere. "But I gotta."

"I know," I replied. "I don't wanna get you in trouble on our first date."

Blake headed up the hill toward her house. I stared into her eyes and kissed her again. A real kiss. A kiss with meaning. I didn't want her to go.

Starship played "Nothing's Gonna Stop Us Now" as she jumped out. I watched as she ran up the short crumbly sidewalk. Bluish flickering light from the T.V. flooded out of the crack as she opened the door and stepped in.

THIRTY-NINE

The old porch swing creaked as I pushed with my right leg and swung my left underneath for momentum. My eyes were still glued to the stretch of street from our driveway down to Grandma's house. The streetlight was on and a thousand bugs were swirling around the top of the pole down on that end of the street.

I hope he shows.

Sammy's lime-green Mustang was almost silent as he rolled around the corner. His tires crunched the gravel as he came to a momentary stop – half on our driveway, half off.

I knew he'd show.

The door opened up for me as I was reaching for the handle. I jumped in.

"Where we headed?" I asked.

"Where the fuck you think?" he said. He was smiling as if he thought I should know.

"Dance?" I questioned.

"Fuckin' A."

I slid into the green bucket passenger side seat and decided to buckle the seat belt. A momentary flash of Simon flying through his window made me do it. We almost never wore them.

Sammy watched but didn't say a word.

I reached in the back seat without looking and opened the cooler. Swirling my hand around in the icy water, I grabbed a beer for both of us from the bottom. I popped his and handed it over. I popped mine and chugged the whole thing in six or eight big gulps. I grabbed another one.

It was just dark enough for the headlights, and the trees beside the road became a blur as we sped out toward loop road. It was only topped with gravel. We swerved from one side to the other as we took the wide turns a little too fast. It was the back way, and the long way, but the dance wouldn't start for another hour. No one ever got there early.

Lynn's parents hadn't let her come to the dance and I felt kind of weird going without her. She'd insisted that I hang with my friends and not let her early curfew ruin my weekend. She'd also insisted that I keep doing things with my friends and not let our relationship change that. The sentiment was sweet, but I felt uneasy about it all. Maybe I should have just stayed home and watched movies with her or something.

We walked through the muddy parking lot toward the old wooden building. There were thousands of fat black crickets swirling around the yellow bulbs along the sides of the building. It was a yearly occurrence. As soon as the first inkling of cold weather made its way down from the north, the crickets began their assault. They covered downtown streets and made their way into any buildings that weren't completely air-tight. They crunched under our feet as we stepped onto the pebbly sidewalk that ran the length of the building.

The song pumping out through the partially open windows was still unrecognizable, but the drumbeats and baseline echoed off the live oaks that outlined the parking lot. My shoes had picked up mud and crickets with each step and I wondered how I'd clean them off before getting on the dance floor. Since the windows weren't closed, maybe the dance floor was already covered with mud and crickets.

We entered the building in our usual manner. Loud, happy, drunk. We'd popped an X before getting out of the car and it was already starting to make my eyes wide and my jaw tight. The energy was starting to surge. Though I'd slammed all of those beers earlier, the little white pill was doing its best to counteract the canned sedative I'd been drinking. We paid at the door, got our hands stamped, and stood in the surging line of drunks working their way up the ramp and into the larger room. Sammy went straight for the beer counter. This was going to be fun. The thought just popped in my mind…

I have a girlfriend.

Lynn and I'd been dating for two weeks. But there was something in my mood. Some rebellion against that control. Her control. She'd *let* me go to the dance. Down deep, I still wanted the excitement of the game. The thrill of the hunt. I needed it. It had become part of me.

The X. The beer. The memories of similar nights in this very dance hall. They all seemed to pull me forward.

I scanned the room and hugged the wall around the left side, toward a mass of familiar faces. The dance floor was already pulsing with bodies and The System was doing their best with Bon Jovi's "You Give Love a Bad Name". I changed my course and slithered through the crowd toward the Smithville contingent. They weren't really dancing, just kind of bumping and swaying back and forth to the beat. A mix of body odor and stale beer met my nose before I was sucked into their vortex.

Sammy caught up just as I was starting to bump and sway with the group. He thrust two beers and two empty Coke cans at me. I pulled myself out of the swirl and ducked into the bathroom. I made a quick transfer of the beer into the empty cans.

I peed, then walked over to the sink. A permanent orangey rust stain started just below the constantly dripping faucet and extended down to the drain. I looked up into the dinged-up mirror. Someone had scratched "Joanie loves Chachi" into the glass.

I have a girlfriend.

I opened my eyes and tried to orient myself. Familiar ceiling. Familiar curtains. My bed. I was home. My thick blood squeezed its way through the tiny capillaries in my brain. The familiar swishing in my ears.

I'm home.

How the fuck did I get here?

I thought back. Leaning against the back wall of the dance hall and talking to some friends from school. I'd gone with Sammy. I'd drank some beer. Faint glimpses of dancing on a crowded dance floor flickered in and out. Bodies but no faces. Music but no songs. A flash here. A flash there.

I need water.

My head swam as I rolled the covers back and sat up on the side of the bed. I slid my feet across the carpet toward the bathroom and clicked on the light. Bad move. I turned the light off and bent over the faucet. I cupped my hand and let the water run through my fingers for a few seconds. When it reached the desired coolness level, I closed my fingers and brought some up to my dry lips. It had that familiar Smithville taste, kind of sweet with a hint of chlorine or pesticide or something. I let a couple sips slide down my parched throat. I stopped short, just as I felt my stomach starting to contract. I stood straight and breathed in slowly. The heave stopped. I waited, took another small sip and looked in the mirror.

My hair was tangled.

My eyes were bloodshot.

You've got to be fucking kidding.

Half way down on the right side of my neck. Dark maroon. Quarter-sized. Faded toward the corners.

A hickey.

Panic hit me immediately and I felt the bile invading my gut. I heaved again. This time I couldn't stop it. I threw up. Once. Twice. Three times. I stood back from the toilet and looked at my fucked-up reflection again.

Holy shit.

It was evidence that someone had intimately sucked my soft neck skin into their mouth. Meaning they had probably been kissing me. Meaning they had probably done other things. I'd never let anyone leave their mark without giving up the goods.

Fuck ...I have a girlfriend.

Maybe she did it?

Maybe I met up with Lynn in town after the dance.

Suddenly, hope filled my heart.

Did I stop by her house?

I could've snuck in her window.

Maybe we finally fucked?

I hoped. I prayed.

I knew better.

I didn't know what to do. I called Sammy.

"What the fuck happened last night?" I asked.

He laughed.

"Same thing that always happens when we go to a dance," he said.

I needed more details than that. I was already thinking of how to lie my way out of the situation. I just didn't have enough information to concoct a story.

Sammy laughed again. Then he told me.

I'd been smashed by the end of the dance. He was ready to go but couldn't find me. None of his early prospects had panned out, so he wanted to go back to town and ride around, or maybe get a party going at the bridge or around Loop Road. He looked all over the dance floor. He'd asked the different groups of folks standing around drinking beer if they'd seen me. Finally, someone told him that I was outside near his car.

He walked out and found me tangled up with an old hookup. We were leaning against his car mugging down. He couldn't give me anymore.

"That's it?" I asked.

"Yep," he said.

"You think we fucked?" I asked nervously.

"Nope," he answered. "Y'all were standing by the car with all your clothes on."

"Really?"

"Yeah," he said. "I had my keys, so you didn't have anywhere to fuck."

Well okay.

The fact that I hadn't had sex was great. But my momentary relief subsided when I remembered the hickey.

Fuck.

How was I going to explain that? I didn't exactly know what had happened, so what was I going to tell Lynn? How could I tell her that we'd only been dating a few weeks and I'd already fucked around? I didn't remember it…but I fucked around.

Shitty feelings suddenly came up from the dark. A numbness began to take over my body. Starting in my toes and fingers, and working its way through my arms and legs, and into my chest…my core. I felt gray and lifeless.

I reached up with my right hand and ran my finger along the old scar. I hadn't had cause to visit the thin red line in a while. I'd been fucked up enough to keep myself pretty numb. But it was still there. Even if it wasn't fresh or visible, it was still there…beckoning.

After a long soak in the shower. I looked in the mirror again. Hickey. Rubbing it with the washcloth had only made it appear brighter, and redder.

Anxiety set in again. The thought tornado had worked on me earlier, as I'd tried to lay back down and force myself back to sleep.

I'm a piece of shit.
I don't deserve her.
She should be with someone else.

My mind assaulted me. The calm loving feelings I'd had for her up until that morning were gone. Only fear and anger remained. Terrified to face her. Angry at myself for ruining it all.

Scared or not, I had to see her. I couldn't stand wondering if she'd already heard something from someone else. Maybe she already knew.

I was almost to the railroad tracks before the turn onto her road and up the hill toward her house. I'd thought about what I might say. Rehearsed the excuses over and over. I was ready.

The crossbar dropped just as I was about to pull across the tracks. The sound of the whistle – single blow, two blows, then another single. The long snaking train bumped and rattled as the cars slowly made their way across in front of me. It seemed to be unusually long. I watched as the different train-cars rocked and rolled on by. Open-topped containers filled with white rock and some with coal. Cylinders filled with oil. Tall, multi-level boxes stacked with layers of new cars and trucks. It was starting to slow, and I hoped it would clear the road before stopping. Sometimes they blocked the road for an hour.

I wouldn't last an hour. I'd worked up the courage to face her, but I needed to do it now.

No. No. I can't do it.

I was too chicken-shit. She hadn't seen me. She didn't know about the hickey. Everything was still good.

I should've turned around. I should've gone back home and avoided her until the hickey went away. But that didn't seem realistic. So, I didn't. The train cleared the track and I stared up the hill. My ears burned and my face glistened with shameful sweat. I had no experience with this kind of situation. But I didn't know what else to do. Something pulled me up the hill toward her. Something about her made me feel different. She knew who I was. She knew I'd wrecked my truck and I drank a little too much. She liked me anyway. She made me feel like I was good. Maybe she even loved me.

I loved her.

The door opened as soon as I pulled up in front of her house. She walked down the short sidewalk without looking up, jumped in the truck, and closed the door without slamming it.

She leaned back and stared at me across the mile-long truck seat. She'd seen it immediately. The way she'd acted, she may have heard about it before I even got there.

I couldn't find words, any words. I didn't know what to say, so I didn't say anything. She looked crushed, disappointed, and frustrated. Then she was mad. Really mad.

"Well I was…" I tried.

Silence.

"I drank too many…" I tried again.

Silence.

"It's Sammy's fault," I said. I took it back immediately.

"I just don't know what happened." I was finally able to get it out.

"But, why?" she asked. Her eyes pleaded. They gave away her disappointment.

"I don't know."

"I don't understand."

"Neither do I."

I knew right then how much I loved her. And, until that conversation I hadn't realized how much it meant to have her love me.

"Why? Just, why?"

She asked me again, and again. I only had the one answer.

"I was drunk," I said flatly. And that was the truth. That was the answer. The only answer. I searched my soul in that moment and that was all I found. I was drunk. I didn't have words for the underlying feelings. The emptiness. The hollowness. The emptiness that could only be filled while I was slamming beer or snorting crank or fucking someone…anyone.

We talked for an hour or so.

"Just give me another chance," I begged.

"It'll never, ever happen again," I swore.

"I'll drink less," I lied.

"You mean the world to me," I promised.

"I love you. I swear to God," I said.

I meant it.

She forgave me.

After a couple of days, everything returned to normal. We hung out after school every day. We went out for pizza. We went to a couple movies. We watched movies and TV shows at her house and at mine. We sat next to each other in my truck as we rode the drag and drove around town. As long as she sat next to me things felt relaxed and comfortable.

FORTY

And then it all crumbled again. Different girl. Different place. Different ending. It was more than just a hickey.

I woke up next to someone. Someone I knew but hadn't anticipated sleeping with. I had a girlfriend.

We lay on soggy cold sheets. I was naked. She was naked.

Visions of the night before flickered in and out of view. She'd stared at me across the bonfire at a party. We were drinking Jim Beam straight from the bottle.

She ended up on top of me, in her bed, at her sister's shitty little apartment.

I almost lost the contents of my stomach as I thought back to the earlier part of the evening. I'd hung out at Lynn's and we'd had a great time doing nothing. We loved just hanging out. I felt safe and accepted with her. She was soft with me. There were no sharp edges. She laughed at all my jokes. She made me feel normal. She was the only person capable of filling that empty space in my chest, without fucking me. Just her presence made it all seem real.

I'd left her house around eleven o'clock, headed for home. I was almost ready to turn, left and up Short Street, when headlights flashed me. I pulled around the block to see who it was and what they wanted.

It was Sammy.

"Dude," he said.

"Dude," I answered.

"You should hop in and cruise for a while."

"Dude I gotta get home."

"So…you're pussy-whipped?"

I assured him I was not.

I jumped in. The windows were down, and the long blondish tips of my hair blew around from behind my neck and brushed my cheeks. Cool and the Gang cranked "Misled" from the two Pioneer six-by-nines mounted in his back dash as we made one more trip up and down the drag and sped out of town. Exhilaration. Excitement. A touch of mischief. I didn't know where we were going at the time, but I knew I should have been home instead.

I woke up a different person. I woke up a cheater. A real cheater. I'd validated every shitty thought I'd ever had about myself, in one boozed evening. I'd proven to myself that I was deserving of all the guilty shameful feelings I carried around with me. And I'd proven it to everyone else. They'd all find out soon enough.

I knew I would lie.

A certain sense of guilt and shame had always seemed to be there. It was just inherent in me. Something deep down that just was. I felt it. I knew it. It was real. But now I'd given it a face. I'd given it a name.

Cheater.

Liar.

I slid gently from under the zebra striped comforter. She was half under the covers, half exposed. I hadn't seen her the night before. It had been dark and we played everything by feel. She was super thin and tan. She had white boobs.

Shame.

The wondering if I was bad, or what might have been wrong with me disappeared. I didn't' have to wonder anymore. I knew.

I knew it. I knew her. We'd had sex. But we'd also been intimate. I needed the love. I needed the validation. And I had to give it to get it. I'd truly felt love. Or what I thought was love. I'd felt her energy as she moaned my name. I'd looked into her eyes and assured her she wasn't just another one-night stand. In that moment, I'd meant it. I'd needed to say it.

I decided to walk the few blocks home instead of calling Sammy to come get me. My truck was at his house, but the thought of talking to him turned my stomach.

I walked. I thought. It wasn't good.

It would only get worse.

I was going to lie to Lynn's face. Well, first on the phone, then to her face. I was going to tell her I'd gone to the party and gone straight home after. It was hard to keep secrets in Smithville, but I had a suspicion that the girl I'd just left had kept these kinds of secrets before.

Weariness crept in as I plodded down the street. Not so much physical. My mind was tired.

The big elm greeted me as I got close. I walked up the front steps and let myself in. I didn't slam the screen door, even though it didn't matter. No one was home. Mom was at church and Dad was out. My stomach was on low vibrate mode. It didn't come up, but it had a slight buzzing feeling that I couldn't shake. I slumped on the couch while Marty Stouffer momentarily distracted me with his detailed description of the mating habits of big horn sheep. It didn't last long though.

My mind quickly made the leap from the mating sheep to my mating activities the night before. I'd acted like an animal. I'd made contact with the female and had mated with her as if on instinct. It was reflexive – as if my body did what it knew to do. I'd felt connected to her up until the moan in my ear. Up until my body seized and stiffened. I left all the emotion and connection there inside her. And then it was gone.

It was scary. I was an animal. I was out of control. But more than that, I felt like shit. I was shit.

And, I had a girlfriend.

FORTY-ONE

I laid the small black box down in front of her. She just stared at it flatly. My palms began to moisten when I saw the conflicted look on her face. The slow seconds ticked by.

"I can't believe it's been a year," I said.

"Me neither," she rolled her eyes.

I knew I was on precarious footing. We'd only been back together for a week. The sting of the latest drunk-bitch outing was still present in the line across her brow. She was here and doing her best to act like things were okay.

"I love you," I said. My voice cracked a little.

"You too," she was looking down at the medium pizza between us. She started to say something else but stopped before any sound came out.

She looked up questioningly, as if saying, "Are you really gonna do this?"

I am.

I'm really gonna do this.

I'd been feeling my hold on her loosening. Each time I'd fucked up, she'd come back. But each time she came back, I got less and less of her. It's as if I was chipping away at something inside her. Or maybe I was building something up. Each fuck-up was another brick in a wall around her heart. I knew it would become too high to climb if I didn't get my shit straight.

She finally reached out and picked up the little velvet container. She gently pried the lid up with her thumb.

I held my breath as the hair-thin gold chain dripped out of her hand. She held it by both ends so that it extended to full length. The small gold heart managed a twinkle, even in the shitty Pizza Hut fluorescence.

I'd gone over her possible reactions in my mind a hundred times. One minute she was smiling and telling me she loved it. She'd reached across the table and hugged my neck – hanging on for dear life. The next, she was throwing the box, and our relationship, across the room. I imagined it bouncing and rolling, coming to a teetering stop just below the plastic leg of the salad bar.

She did neither.

"Put it on me," her voice was soft.

"Okay."

A cool wave of relief washed over me. I could feel the clammy sweat on my hands and under my arms start to dissipate.

"No more shit?" she half-smiled.

"Promise," I said. "I really mean it this time."

And I did. I really meant it.

"Give me a ride to work tomorrow?" she asked with a crooked smile.

"You know I will." I said. "But only if I get to pick you up after."

"Well…I guess."

We both laughed out loud. I'd been dropping her off and picking her up from her supermarket job for most of the last three months…when we were together. She usually got off late. The highway was always empty. It was our time. Our quiet alone time.

"I love you more than anyone I've ever known," I said.

"I know," she said.

I kissed her gently.

"I'll pick you up in the morning."

"Okay."

"Love you."

"You too."

I just stood there for a long while and bathed in the rightness of the moment. We were good. It was good.

FORTY-TWO

Sammy tossed me a Miller Lite as I walked out onto the slatted wooden dock from the parking lot. I'd just dropped Lynn off at work and hauled ass to the lake to meet him and the guys for some skiing and sun.

"We were just about to leave you, dude," he said.

"I guess I'd have swum out and found you," I said with a laugh.

"Yeah. You probably would."

I stepped onto the old bass-boat as our buddy tried to hold it still next to the dock. It bobbed up and down as the rolling wake of a passing boat crashed into the side of ours. The brown outdoor carpet on the bow felt good under my feet. I slid across gently, so I wouldn't topple over the side with the next wave.

"Let's roll bitches," Sammy shouted as he held his beer up.

"Wooooooo hooooooooo," I answered.

Our buddy pushed the throttle down as far as it would go. The motor responded and the whole boat seemed to jump out of the water. We planed out on top of the water quickly and shot across the lake like a jet. My hair whipped the back of my neck. I closed my eyes and let the wind kiss my cheeks. The beer tasted as good as it ever had. Smooth. Sweet. Bubbly.

Sammy handed me another just as my empty can rattled into place with the others in the bottom of the boat.

We rounded the bend and slowed to a float as we entered our favorite cove. The Boy Scout camp was located back in the woods. The boat lurched lower in the water as we slowed to an idle. I tied our rope to a

203

cable connected to the walking bridge the scouts had built across the narrowest part of the inlet.

There were three or four other boats already tied up…and lots of girls floating and bobbing around. Some were clothed. Some were not.

I dove in and went down until I felt a change in the water temperature. My fingers brushed the tops of the underwater weeds as I exhaled and watched the bubble stream rise upward until it reached the surface. As soon as my head was back above water, I saw her watching me.

She smiled and looked away. I'd known her forever, but never really noticed her. Not like this. Her beautiful white smile sharply contrasted her perfectly tanned skin. The sun had made the tips of her incredibly blonde hair even blonder.

My lunge-jump back into the boat was awkward at best. I glanced to see if she was looking. She was not. The cooler squawked as I opened the top and grabbed a beer. The cold foam felt good as it spewed on my chest. They had been shaken pretty good on the wild ride over.

I slammed it in five or six easy gulps. I did the same to the next two.

There was a collective *Wooooo hooooo* from the crowd when I burped. After slamming three beers, it was a pretty spectacular burp.

When I looked up, she was staring me down. She hung onto a rope that was tied to the handrail of the bridge. Her head and shoulders rolled gently above the water's surface. I balanced on the edge of the boat and calculated the best location for the awesome cannonball I was about to do. I wanted to get maximum splash on anyone who was near enough.

Her eyes were still locked onto me as I jumped. I squeezed my legs up as high as I could and held them there tightly with my arms. My chin was tucked just right. The water plunked my head and face as it rushed back in on top of me. I let go of the hold on my legs and stayed down as long as I could. I wasn't sure what I'd do if she was still looking at me when I surfaced.

I hoped she was.

Our eyes were glued to one another as I did my best dog paddle in her direction. I tried to think of something clever to say as I closed the distance. I just kissed her instead.

I could feel their eyes on us as we slid under the bridge. They all knew I had a girlfriend. Most of them knew that girlfriend.

I held on to a slick weathered piece of wood with one hand, and her with the other. We bobbed up and down with the gently rolling water.

We kissed.

We touched.

She stopped me as my hand found its way under her swimsuit.

"What about Lynn?" she asked.

"She's at work."

"Aren't y'all back together?"

"Yeah."

"Then, we can't."

"Come on. We've already started."

"Yeah, but we can't"

"You sure? Come on."

"We can mess around, but I won't fuck you."

I tried anyway.

She was true to her word.

We kissed and felt and rubbed and squeezed. We sucked the air from each other's lungs in long passionate kisses.

"I think I love you," I said suddenly.

"Fuck you," she said with a giggle. "You have a girlfriend and you love her."

"Yeah...but I think I love you too."

"Well, that's too bad."

We made our way back over by the boat and drank more beers. We kissed some more. Everyone seemed drunk and no one seemed interested in what we were doing.

"What time is it?" I asked no one in particular.

"Seven-thirty," someone said.

"Fuck. Fuck. Fuck," I said. "I gotta pick Lynn up at nine."

"So, you're just going to leave?" she asked.

"You're the one that was all worried about Lynn," I said

"Yeah, but you can't just leave now," she answered. "You never know what might happen."

"But you said...."

"Yeah. I'm drunker now."

Fuck. Fuck. Fuck.

The thought popped into my head out of nowhere. I knew how

shitty it was before I even set the plan in motion. But I was going to do it. I had to do it.

I lunge-jumped in the boat.

"Be right back," I yelled to the crowd.

"Hey…my fucking boat," I heard my buddy's voice as I sped out of the cove.

I hoped he was home. The plan wouldn't work if he wasn't.

I could see the neon sign as I neared the dock.

Open.

I docked the boat, made a quick loop around a post with the tie rope, and sprinted up the grassy hill to the shitty little convenience store. The sign next to the door read "No shirt, no shoes, no problem."

"Can I please use your phone?" I was out of breath. "It's…it's an emergency."

"There's a payphone outside," she answered. The dangling cigarette looked as if it was glued to her bottom lip and would slip off any second.

"Please? I don't have any cash."

"Well…" she smiled when she said it.

"I'll make it quick. I promise"

I called my brother Josh and asked him to go pick Lynn up from work.

"I'm at the lake and the boat is broken down all the way back at the Boy Scout camp," I told him. "Just go pick her up and take her home."

"Seriously?" he said

"Yeah. Just fucking do it?" I begged.

"Okay. But you owe me big time."

"Anything man. Anything you want."

I stayed. I stayed and tried to be in love with the girl at the lake while my brother picked my girlfriend up from work, lied to her for me, and took her home.

The girl still wouldn't fuck me.

I woke up early the next morning. No hangover. The cool humidity hung just above the grass as I slid my bare feet along the side of the street. One glance over, that was all. His house. I didn't know what I was looking for, it was just kind of an instinct.

Z-Bo was happy to see me as usual. He jumped up and down on his hind legs as I unchained the gate and walked through. We stared at each other for a count of three, frozen. Like a shot, we both took off at a dead sprint. He always beat me to the tree. His muscles rippled as he grabbed and pulled at the knotted rope I threw over the lowest limb. I pulled hard and his feet just barely cleared the ground. His jaws locked, tugging and jerking with all he had. His body twisted around in circles like a caterpillar about to emerge from its cocoon. When he was done, we wrestled on the back porch for a few minutes and then I ate some cereal with Grandma.

"He's almost out of dog food," she said.

"Really?"

"Yeah, he eats like a horse."

"I'll grab some from town later. I gotta get home now."

I had to get home and call Lynn. She slept until ten o'clock on weekends. It was ten-thirty. Z-Bo had helped me forget what had gone down at the lake the day before. I woke up worried but talked myself into a smile. The crew we'd partied with seemed pretty cool and I hoped they were tight-lipped.

I shuffled my bare feet back toward home and purposely didn't look over this time. Up the front steps and into the living room.

"Don't slam the door," Mom said, just as the screen slammed behind me.

"Sorry."

She was smiling when I walked in the kitchen.

"Going to get some dog food later," I said. "Grandma said Z-Bo eats like a horse."

"He's as big as a horse," she laughed.

I dialed the number and stretched the tangled chord as far as it would go into the other room.

"Is Lynn up?"

"Yes." The voice was cold and flat.

"Can I please talk to her?"

"Hold on."

She was crying when she got on the phone.

"What the...what the fuck is wrong with you?" she sobbed.

"We didn't do anything," I said.

"Bull…bull shit."

"But we didn't."

"How do you think I found out?" she was angry now.

"What are you talking about?"

"She fucking called me this morning and told me everything."

"What?" I was genuinely shocked.

Maybe she's bluffing?

"She said she was drunk and she felt bad and she liked me as a friend and knew I'd find out anyway."

"So, I guess she told you we didn't fuck?"

"Really? Are you fucking serious right now?"

"We didn't. I swear."

"Are you…are you that stupid?" She was sobbing again. "You fucking told her you loved her."

I went silent. I had nothing. It was true. I'd been drunk but not shit-faced. I remembered everything. I did tell her I loved her. And I would have fucked her if she'd been willing.

Goddamit.

What the fuck IS wrong with me?

"But I was drunk," I stammered. It was all I could come up with. It was usually all I could come up with.

"Just hear me out. Give me a chance," I pleaded.

"You've had way too many chances," she said honestly. "I've wasted a whole year of my life with you."

"Please?"

"No," she said with no emotion. "I don't deserve this shit."

"Please? I'll change. I love you." My voice turned raspy with desperation.

"No." It sounded so final.

That word. No. It was a mule-kick to the chest. I exhaled and couldn't find another breath. She hung up as I was starting to say whatever it was I was going to say next. It didn't really matter. There were no words. I'd done it again. This time there was no doubt, no lying my way out of it.

Fuck. Why'd she have to tell?

I gently placed the phone down on the hook, grabbed my keys off the table and walked out of the house like a zombie. The screen door slammed behind me.

I came to my senses after three days of shit-faced, blacked-out drinking. I'd just left Mom's disappointed face standing on the porch wondering where I'd been. Now I found myself in a nervous panic, driving up the hill toward Lynn's house. I didn't know why. Something pulled me up there.

Heartbroken. I'd let her down again. I'd let myself down again. It seemed I was always letting someone down again.

I stopped the truck on the street adjacent to her room. The moon ducked and weaved through the soft clouds streaming in from the south. My muscles tensed. I got out and eased across the freshly mown lawn. I sat and pressed my back against the warm wall below her window. She was there. I could almost feel her breathing. The checkered pattern of brown and grey bricks was all that separated us. That, and the million miles of emptiness pouring from my heart.

If I knocked, would she ease the window up like she had before? Would she let me climb in and have my way? Maybe turn on the closet light and drop the t-shirt, just so I could see her body before I had her? Could we do to each other what we'd done so many times before? Would she let me desperately love her, the only way I knew how?

I longed to lay there tangled in the sheets and sweat and breathe her in again? I'd had my last chance. Even the last chance had been one too many.

How many?

How many times had I done this to her? She was so sweet and loving. All she wanted was to love me.

Memories washed over me. Her smiling face looking back at me from the front of the boat on our last fishing trip. The sarcastic way she rolled her eyes when I put in the same Def Leppard cassette, over and over and over. The look of delight when I ordered a Canadian bacon and mushroom pizza without even asking her. The heat and pain on her face when she knew I was lying…when she knew where I'd been the night before. The disgust in her voice when she told me for the thousandth time that it didn't matter that I was drunk.

It didn't matter.

I knew it was over.

I rocked up onto my knees and kissed the wall where I knew her head would be. The grass had become wet from a heavy dew while I sat there. I shuffled back across the yard and slid onto the cool vinyl seat.

I was so close to her. I didn't want to leave.

Tesla started in with their heart-breaking opening to "Love Song". I lifted my sleeve. The thin red line was there. It had become permanent. Sometimes the scar looked like the pink seam of my t-shirt. Other times it looked like a jagged cut I'd sustained in a knife fight. The appearance depended on how violent my mood had been the last time. It was mine. I only visited occasionally these days, but it was mine. It would always be mine.

When the intro was over, and the vocals began ...*So you think that it's over. That your love has finally reached the end...* I glanced at her window again. She was there. Just her and her t-shirt. She still loved me. That made it worse.

The blade was cold as it touched my skin.

I pressed.

It cut.

I tasted the salt as the tears made their way over my top lip and down toward my chin. I traced the line again with the blade. The warm stream turned cold as it reached my elbow. A couple of drips. Tears. Blood. I glanced at the house again. It was over. I eased it in gear and let it roll forward, down the slight grade toward the end of the block. *Loves gonna find a way back to you. I know. I know. I know. I know.*

FORTY-THREE

I opened the tiny zippy and dipped in the end of the Bic ballpoint cap. Tiny brownish white grains rolled down my shirt and onto my jeans. I licked my finger and smashed the sticky little bits and immediately sucked them off. I'd poured it onto the mirror the night before, chopped it as finely as I could with a new blade, and gently poured it back in for use the next morning. This morning.

Sometimes it remained separated and sometimes it didn't. This morning it was clumpy. The humidity and the heat from hiding it in my front pocket hadn't helped. I didn't care. I was late for work. I should have pulled out of the driveway a half-hour ago.

My job was easy, but I couldn't drink. I rode in most days with my boss and his son, who was a school mate and buddy. And, the job sometimes required me to operate a bulldozer or backhoe. I didn't want to do that drunk.

I was late, but I'd called and told them I was on my way.

This was only my second job since high school. College had only lasted a few months and hadn't gone well. Beer. Women. Fishing. I dropped all my classes and decided I needed to work.

Eighteen years old. I needed gas money. I needed beer money. I needed money for tiny zippies.

I had a job. I had a truck. And somewhat of a routine.

Lynn and I were on and off again…again. Things with her weren't optimal, but at least she still went out with me every once in a while. We'd broken up for the last time, a few times. It always felt permanent. Things were really never the same after the girl at the lake. She never really forgave me.

I never forgave me.

I drank a lot.

A lot.

I snorted the little puff of sticky powder from the end of the pen cap. It hit my right nostril with the usual sting. The right nostril was my go to. Sometimes if it bled I'd snort with the left, but it somehow felt different. It always felt like some got stuck in my sinuses and never made it down the left side. So right it was.

Snort.

Burn.

Tears.

Burn.

Drainage.

Swallow.

Boom. On my empty stomach, my heart-rate sped up almost immediately.

I ducked down and peered through the clear spot in the broken windshield. It was shattered in a spider-web pattern from the center out to the edges. Tiny crystals covered the dashboard like shiny diamond dust.

Lynn had been riding around with another dude the weekend before and I'd immediately and reactively punched the glass. She wasn't completely mine anymore. She was barely mine at all. It stung. My stomach had immediately tried to come up but I'd been able to hold it to a heave. It was only the second time I'd seen her with someone else. The jealousy had come from some dark place way down inside me that I'd only glimpsed a couple times before. It bubbled up at first. Just bubbled from the pit of my stomach and percolated its way up through my body. It settled in my mind…and didn't leave. Not for one second of my day. I was consumed with her and what she might be doing with someone else. It wasn't so much that she was trying to move on, but the fact that I was the reason.

Love.

Jealousy.

Anger.

I rolled into my foreman's driveway. He and his son were sitting in the old red Chevy. The diesel engine rattled and the defroster tried to remove some of the humidity from the windows. I threw my little red square Igloo in the back and jumped in. The talk radio news guys were discussing the recent heatwave. A tinny voice mentioned another week of hundred plus temps. It was going to be hot. It had already been hot.

We drove up to the job site and loaded the supplies for the day. Shovels. Only shovels. We'd be digging the little trenches, or footings, for the bottom edge of the concrete ditches that would run along the edge of the highway. We'd be digging in the heat.

We'd left the shade of the lay-down yard immediately and shoveled yards of dirt out of a long skinny ditch. We worked until well after our usual lunch break so we'd be ready for the cement truck to deliver an extra load. Unbearable heat assaulted me. As if I was standing too close to a big camp fire. Except it wasn't like a camp fire. The heat surrounded my body instead of the usual one-sided heat from a campfire.

My shovel was brand new. The shiny yellow handle still had the white sticky label on it, just above the silvery-grey shovel head. My cloth glove caught a corner of the label and made a clicking noise every time I slid my hand down.

I stuck the point of the sharp shovel into the hard clay surface and placed my right foot on the little flat step. Bouncing up with rhythm, my left foot hit the other side just right. With my entire weight balanced on the two steps, the shovel teetered, just a bit, and sliced off a six-inch piece of the clay. Before the flat red piece of dirt was able to tip forward and fall, I deftly jumped off and swung the shovel up. The squarish clod made a nice thud as it landed up on the bank. This had been my cadence all morning. Point. Jump. Slice. Pitch. Thud. Repeat.

Just shoveling. It was the kind of unfocused work that allowed my mind to wander. Some days I could push my thoughts over to fishing or hunting or having sex, or drinking, or snorting crank, or campfires. But lately, when I wasn't imagining Lynn fucking some other guy, I was thinking about my death.

Sometimes I'd daydream about it for an hour or so before I realized what I was thinking: lying in the seat of my truck after smashing it into a tree; mangled at the bottom of a cliff, with my truck wrapped around me; the flames of a glorious fire engulfing me and taking me out in a blaze of glory. Some grand, dramatic exit. Not scary. Comforting. Warm.

I was robotically pitching dirt from the trench while envisioning my friends peering down into my coffin, when I suddenly snapped out of it.

What the fuck?

It's so damn hot.

My brain felt as if it were spinning behind my eyes. It was kind of like a dizzy headache, without the ache. Someone had flushed a toilet and the water was swirling around inside my head. I looked down at my shovel.

Why is the handle crooked?

Did I break it?

It was fiberglass. I didn't remember breaking it.

Then there was light – two horizontal slits.

What the fuck?

Where am I?

As the slits grew bigger, I realized my eyes had been closed.

Bright.

I tried to shield my eyes from the sun with my hand and make sense of the scene around me. But as I lifted my hand off the ground, I felt all the water inside my head move to one side and I lost my balance. I sat on the ground with my legs laying out to my right. Four or five people stood around staring down at me. My boss and his son were crouched near me and seemed to be saying words. They made no sense, so I didn't try to answer. I just sat there and looked around.

The words finally sounded familiar.

"How do you feel?" my boss asked.

I wasn't sure.

"Did something hit you in the head?"

I didn't know.

My body didn't feel any pain, so I dismissed that thought.

"Do you want some water?"

I didn't.

"Here, you need some water."

I puked. All over my legs. "Should we call an ambulance?" another worker asked excitedly.

"No," I replied.

They loaded me up in the red Chevy and took me to the ER.

Heat stroke. One minute I was using a shovel. The next minute I was lying on my back. I didn't remember anything but the crooked shovel handle. My favorite backhoe operator had been excavating a trench nearby and noticed me sprawled on the ground. Luckily, he hadn't backed over me. Julio had jumped off of the machine and limped-walked-hopped over to where I lay. It was almost a hop, because of his bum leg. A few years earlier, while unloading a trailer full of 36-inch diameter concrete drainage pipes, his leg had been destroyed. The pipes had rolled off of the end of the trailer and right over the lower section of his leg. It had been crushed, in many places. Now, the leg was bent in an outward arc and he limp-walk-hopped on the outer front portion of his foot. He was straight from Mexico, so when they told him he had no recourse but to let the ER doctor splint it and let it heal, that's what he did. It healed badly. But, at least they made him an operator.

"Don't feel sorry for me, Amigo," he'd said. "I usually sit anyways."

We were silent on the short bumpy ride to the hospital. The passenger side AC vent shot ice-cold air directly in my face. The middle one was aimed at my torso and felt as if it was turning my sweat-soaked shirt into ice.

I objected to the wheelchair ride from the truck into the ER.

"I can walk," I said.

"No," the nurse answered. "It's mandatory."

"Heat stroke," the doctor said. "It's super-hot outside. Record hot. Like 112 degrees Fahrenheit hot."

It was ice cold in the ER though. I shivered as a nurse released my arm from the BP cuff. She'd put it on too tight and now my fingers tingled.

"You boys shouldn't be working out in this heat anyway," she said.

I tried to make sense of what he'd just told me. *Heat stroke.* But all I could think about was whether or not they knew I had done crank that morning.

"Any prescription drugs?" he asked.

"Nope."

My mind raced.

Does he know?

Can he tell?

Will he figure out that I drink? Smoke weed? Snort crank? On a regular basis?

He didn't mention them and he didn't ask. If he'd asked, I would have assured him that I was not doing any of those things.

I got to stay home for two days, and then light duty for a couple weeks. No outside work for a week. No outside work for the week after if the temperature was above 85 degrees. The temperature was always above 85, so I spent the next two weeks in the tiny trailer answering phones which almost never rang.

I enjoyed the air conditioning. And I had time to talk to Lynn on the phone every now and then. I clung to the hope that we'd get back together someday even though I knew she should hate me.

"Nope. I still love you," she'd promised the day before as I stared at an old Farmer's Almanac on the trailer wall.

The trailer was quiet and lifeless when everyone was out on the site working. My mind teetered back and forth between sanity and cooped up craziness.

Scenarios of her and a new guy pierced my heart. So real. They always said loving, kind things to each other. They always had soft, loving sex.

That should be me.

He wasn't a cheater. He never lied. Or drank. He didn't snort crank. No weed. And he didn't cut himself.

He's everything I'm not.

She'll be sorry when I'm gone.

She'll miss me and realize how much I love her.

It'll be too fucking late.

Then I was in the coffin again. She looked down. No words. Just tears. I tasted them as they fell on my face and ran across my lips.

"I should have taken you back," she'd say. "I wish I could tell you I love you…just once."

Good.

But you can't…you'll never be able to again.

Vindication.

Relief.

FORTY-FOUR

My two weeks of light duty crawled by. I was done with this job. I didn't want to go back out into the heat and dig more ditches or pour more concrete or flag more traffic or clean out more curbs or any of that shit. The boring daily tasks allowed my mind to wander too much. There was just too much time to think.

I'd grown accustomed to hanging out in the trailer and soaking up the conditioned air. I didn't like the trailer, but I didn't like digging ditches either. My mind had become bored and consumed with thoughts of how I could die. I was starting to feel like I might be crazy...and I talked to myself most of the day.

I'd worked that job for two years, maybe a little longer, and I was ready to do something else. I wasn't sure what, but not that. I had to find a job that made me think about something...anything. Something that would keep my mind occupied.

I'll feel better then.

But I couldn't just quit. I had to pay for gas, food, beer, and drugs. I couldn't leave without another job.

Mom and Dad would be disappointed. I'd disappointed them enough. They wanted me to have a job with insurance and good pay. I worked hard and made decent money for someone just out of high school. They'd become accustomed to me buying my own gas and any food I ate while out partying. They did not know that most of that money went toward beer and drugs. My truck was usually running on fumes. My body was the same.

217

An idea hit me as I sat in the trailer on an overcast Tuesday morning. The remnants of last night's rain were still dripping from the cracked corner of the roof just outside the dirty window. Some guys were outside, busy fueling their equipment for the day. No one had gone out to check the site yet. If it was too wet, the work day would be called off. Some guys would hang around the yard and organize tools and supplies, but most would leave immediately and grab a twelve-pack on their way home. I would fall into the latter category.

As I watched Julio hop-walking around the yard, cleaning this, moving that, I envisioned myself laying on the ground near the scattered pile of wooden forms that they'd used for pouring concrete the week before. That's when the idea struck me. A way to quit, without actually quitting.

Chunks of mud dropped off my foreman's boots as he made his way up the newly repaired wooden steps and into the little front room of the trailer. I smiled.

"You enjoying the clouds?" I asked.

"You bet. Anything's better than that damn heat."

"I think I'm ready to move back outside." I wasn't lying when I mentioned that I had been feeling caged up in the tiny capsule of a trailer and that I wanted to be back out with the crew.

I knew what I was going to do. My heart raced as I thought it through. I wasn't sure if I could pull it off, but I knew I was going to try.

After five more days in the trailer, I was finally allowed back to light duty work outside. I'd had plenty of time to perfect my plan and had even practiced a couple of times at home. We'd all hung around the yard on Monday, attempting to dry things out. I'd felt the panic set in when I realized we weren't going out on the job site that day. I'd planned on doing it the first day back outside. I was ready.

The second day back was dry enough to work. Julio was meticulously digging the ditch that would hold the forty-eight-inch drain pipes. The banana yellow backhoe was humming at full speed as he spun it around and flung the dirt into a perfect pile behind him. The same dirt would be used to cover the pipes when we were done. The pipes were stacked neatly on a trailer, waiting for him to flatten the bottom of the trench. He was the best operator on site and could make the bottom of a ditch so smooth that someone could roll a quarter down its length as if it were on a concrete sidewalk. We would attach a long heavy chain to the little cable loop on top of each pipe and unload them, one by one. The operator would then move over to the other side of the ditch and drop them in their final resting place.

I waited nervously for my opportunity. I wasn't sure when it would come, but I felt like I'd know when it was time. I'd been going over it in my mind all morning. I'd planned on doing it before lunch, but I panicked twice as I was about to go through with it. I'd never done anything like this. My palms dripped and I knew that anyone within a hundred feet could probably hear my heart beating. The rhythm of the backhoe was smooth. Dig. Scoop. Spin. Drop. Dig. Scoop. Spin. Drop. The other guys had walked over to the trailer to begin unloading the pipes.

It was time.

I glanced around and checked behind me. No one watching.

Picking the softest spot possible in the rocky soil, I laid down and curled my legs back behind me. I had to make them look random, as if they just happened to have landed that way when I fell. I half-placed, half-tossed the shovel into place. Not too close, but far enough so that it would seem to have fallen that way.

Get the fuck up. Why are you doing this?

Why couldn't I just tell Mom and Dad I was leaving? Why couldn't I just find another job? I knew the answer. Something was wrong with me.

It only took a couple minutes. Julio was in mid-swing when he saw me. The noise from the machine went from a high-pitched hum to a low rumble. His door clicked when it opened and banged behind him. My heart was a drum. A big loud bass drum.

I counted. One. Two. Three. Four. Five.....twenty-six. It only took him twenty-six seconds to hop-walk the distance from the trench to the area where I was crumpled on the ground.

"Amigo?" He sounded scared. "Amigo?"

I let him shake me a few times before cracking my eyes open. My body tingled as I played the part...just as it had the first time I'd really passed out.

"Amigo? You okay?"

I stared at him as if I didn't understand.

When I finally spoke, it was low and slow, just like they'd told me I had that fist time. The foreman and a couple other workers were running over, just as I was beginning to answer his questions.

The ER doc was perplexed. He'd been sure I had passed out from heat exhaustion or heat stroke the last time I'd visited him. But now he wasn't sure. He thought it could be seizures. I wasn't exhibiting the signs of heat stroke this time. My temperature wasn't high enough and it hadn't been over ninety degrees all week. He just wasn't sure what to do.

He ordered some tests. I hoped my panic didn't show when he was discussing the panel of blood work. Test results showing alcohol didn't bother me and wouldn't have bothered Mom and Dad.

Crank.

Weed.

Those would bother everyone. My breath shortened.

This wasn't going as planned. I'd expected to just pass out and say I was going home. But the foreman insisted I go to the ER again. Not just because he cared about me, but because it was company policy. Anyone who was injured on the job had to go the ER. And even though this wasn't a real "injury", I had to go anyway.

What the fuck? Blood tests.

This could be worse than quitting. If Mom and Dad knew I did drugs, things would never be the same.

I stretched my arm out as the nurse tightened the rubber strap just below my right bicep.

"Squeeze the ball now," she said as she stuck the needle into my bulging vein. The almost fresh cut on my left arm tingled.

Terror squeezed my throat as she released the strap. Thick maroon blood filled the clear glass tube. I knew what was in that blood.

A little later, another nurse squeezed gooey cold gel on little white pads then stuck them to the tiny areas she'd just shaved on my chest. She hooked me up to the EKG machine with a smile.

I went through all kinds of tests. Everyone was perplexed. None of the tests showed anything. And I knew why. I was the only one who knew why.

I'm not sick.

But I was.

I couldn't define it. But deep down I was beginning to believe…something just wasn't right.

I spent most of that next two weeks at home watching T.V. The doctor had recommended that I not go back to work until we knew what the tests indicated. He was sure it was some kind of seizure. And even though they'd drawn my blood, more than once, they never mentioned anything about drugs. I never asked.

Normal people don't do shit like this.

Why don't I just end it all and make everyone happy?

I'd seen myself in that coffin a hundred times. It felt good to think about it. It felt right.

The sweat was once again a constant on my hands, feet and pits. My heart seemed to beat fast all the time, even when I wasn't doing crank. I hadn't done any drugs since I'd had to take those blood tests after fake passing out. I was afraid I'd have to do more.

The lie had gotten so big that I couldn't back out now. I was all in. I was an actor.

I lied to my parents. I lied to Lynn. I lied to my friends and coworkers and bosses. And I lied to the doctors. I wasn't even sure what was true anymore.

I answered the doctor's questions with genuine frustration on my face. He shuffled some papers and moved one from the front of his clipboard to the back. His furrowed brow showed his frustration.

"We're done."

"What?" I asked.

"There's nothing else we can do." He said without emotion. "If it happens again, we'll start over."

They couldn't figure it out. They couldn't quite put a finger on it. They knew all the things it wasn't, but just weren't sure what it was. Test after test ruled out this and that possibility. I'd spent a lot of time in his office. I'd spent two weeks at home with a gadget and some wires attached to me.

"You probably shouldn't stay at that job," he said. "There's heavy equipment everywhere and too much risk to you and others."

Holy shit.

I hadn't planned on it taking that long. I didn't think they'd run all those tests and ask all those questions. I hadn't really thought it all through. But there it was. My plan had worked in the end. I was done.

FORTY-FIVE

The smell drifted in through the crack in my door and made its way down
into my breathing hole. Some mornings I still woke up with the comforter
over my head and face, just like when I was little. Only a tiny hole for my
nose and mouth. So, whatever was in the dark couldn't get me.

Bacon.

"Breakfast is ready," Mom said.

Silence.

"Bacon and eggs and toast."

"Okay," I mumbled. "Be there in a minute."

My palms dripped as I got dressed. Excitement and nervousness
fought for top position in my mind. I shoved the little bag down into the
right front pocket of my cheap navy-blue dress pants. I'd spent half of the
check from my last week at the bridge company and bought myself a couple
grams. I'd decided to switch from crank to coke for a while because of a
consistent nose bleed I'd acquired. I knew it wouldn't be a permanent
switch. But if I could afford it for a little while, I'd do it. Coke seemed to go
down a bit smoother and didn't seem to burn my nose and sinuses quite as
badly. I thought the nose bleeds might stop if I stayed away from the crank
for a couple days or maybe a week.

This was a huge day. While I'd been home on light duty, I'd also
been looking around for a better way to spend my work days. Mom had
heard about a nice opportunity at a local bank. She knew someone there
and got me an interview.

"Why are you leaving your current job?" the bank manager had asked.

"I had a heat stroke," I said. "And, I'm looking for something a little more professional."

She called the next day.

"You have the job."

No more digging ditches and no more thirty-minute drive to work. I was going to dress nicely. I was going to work with the public. I would get to hang out in the air-conditioned lobby most of the day. Even though I felt like I needed the drugs and most days a few drinks, I felt uplifted. Positive. I couldn't wait.

I jumped in my truck and settled into the seat. My nerves. I had to calm my nerves. I dumped the baggie out onto my little mirror. Only a couple of chops with the edge of my driver's license. Two easy lines. I snorted the closest one – half of the quarter bag. I sniffed deeply, three times, moved the straw, and snorted the other line. My stomach took a couple minutes to settle.

Fumbling through the pile of cassettes next to me on the seat, I found what I was looking for and popped it in. The handle squawked as I rolled down the windows. Motley Crue's "Dr. Feelgood" seemed to reach something way down inside of me. It was the perfect song for pumping myself up...the coke didn't hurt. Checking my nose for powder in the rearview I cranked the music and slammed it in reverse. I left a cloud of dust behind me as I spun out of the driveway. I had a few minutes to ride the drag, so I rewound the tape and let my truck drift robotically up and down the same strip of pavement.

Not sure whether I'm cut out to be a banker.

Not sure if I'm cut out to be anything.

I got off to a decent start. I worked that day in the back with two hot women. Neal, the bank president seemed nice, and he'd invited me out to see his ranch. My heart was a buzz saw from the coke. Even though I was a pretty hyper guy anyway, I hoped no one would notice that I was wired.

Fuck.

I looked the customers in the eye as they came in and handed me their checks. Glancing over at the "do not cash" memo to my right, I verified that they weren't on the naughty list before shuffling out the crisp green bills. Some folks I knew. Some were strangers. But after that first day,

I felt like a professional. The dark pants, white button-down, and tie made me feel like a banker.

I'm a banker.

I can get used to this.

The first couple months came and went. I'd made new friends, counted thousands of dollars, sorted a ton of paperwork, and gone out to the president's place for dinner on two occasions.

I was a natural. I completed all my tasks quickly and actually enjoyed the work. There was even talk of me becoming an appraiser, mostly for the folks that used cattle as collateral for their loans. I was familiar with cattle since we'd had them out at our farm since I was a kid, and Neal thought that was a big plus. I felt awesome.

Then I ran out of crank.

I could only afford a week's worth at a time. I'd snorted up the last little bit of last week's supply on a Saturday night and I didn't have time or money to buy more. I'd slept all day Sunday and now here it was again…Monday.

What the fuck?

I wasn't hung over, but a heavy fog hovered over my head. It was as if the lenses of my eyes had somehow gotten dirty and everything looked hazy. I was staring through a smudgy windshield.

I parked my truck in the back, but I didn't want to go in. I felt like taking off and driving out to the farm, or walking down behind Mom's house, sitting on my little dock, and staring at the river as it rolled by. I decided to do just that. I would get out of there before anyone else showed up.

I'll call in sick.

I didn't care that I was still relatively new. I couldn't go in. I couldn't even make myself open the truck door. I tried listening to music, thinking that may help get me pumped like it had before. "Dr. Feelgood" didn't do it. I popped in another tape. Nope. I tried another, and then another. Nothing.

Fuck.

I put my truck in reverse, turned my head to back up, and saw Neal walking over from his parking spot.

Double fuck.

I turned the truck off and opened the door. I was still a little early, so I hoped he hadn't known I was about to leave.

He smiled. "Come see me in my office a little later?"

"Will do," I said.

Maybe he knew I was high almost every day? Maybe he saw me staring at my co-worker's boobs while she was bending over to pick up the mail bin?

Panic set in. I thought about letting him go on in and then getting the hell out of there. I didn't. I locked my doors and headed in.

What in the hell does he want?

I stared at him. I wasn't sure if he was serious, so I just stared. Our eyes locked for a few seconds and then I stared at the floor. The greyish carpet was worn in front of his desk, and someone had spilled coffee. I looked back up and told him I was in.

Hell yes.

Excitement and a sense of pride rose in my chest.

He wants me to live on his place.

He trusts me.

The president of the bank had just asked me if I wanted to move out onto one of his properties. He owned more than a few, but this one was beautiful. He needed someone out there to look over his cows and take care of some routine maintenance issues. He had a repossessed trailer house sitting behind the other bank building and he proposed moving it out to the ranch just for me. The rent would be cheap. I would have fifty acres all to myself. I would have a place for Z-Bo to run free and I could fish and hunt all I wanted.

What was not to like?

FORTY-SIX

I sat alone in the front room of the little trailer house and stared out the big picture window. The white longhorn bull was grazing with his head down in the knee-high grass just across the fence from my yard. His impressive neck was splashed with rusty brown and red spots and streaks. He lived up to his breed's name. Each horn was three feet long and twisted up just slightly at the end. The tips were nail-sharp and always seemed to glisten when the light hit them just right.

Watching the cattle usually brought some light to bad days. It had been three months since my meeting with the bank president, and the fifty acres had become home. The bull and his girls were a part of that feeling. They were calm and consistent. They ate when they were hungry and drank when they were thirsty. The bull chased the twenty or so cows tirelessly and got lucky quite often.

Life had been okay.

The stale smell from the kitchen had been getting stronger all week. Every morning I smelled it. Every morning I vowed to clean it up when I got home. I knew where it originated. It would have been easy to make it go away.

Most of the dirty dishes in the sink had water standing in them. Water, and differing amounts of leftover food, grease, and scum from meals past. The smell was there, but not strong enough for action yet. At least I could empty the bowls and cups.

I'll do it when I get back home.

I'd been staring out of the window all morning. Just sitting on the little folding chair I sometimes pulled away from the dining table. Not much of a table, just a shitty little fold-up with rust stains on cracked blue vinyl. It sat in the middle of the living room floor. The walls were mostly bare, with the exception of my Iron Maiden poster and a pin up calendar I'd scored from a buddy. An overused tan couch took up space along the longest wall in the place. The cushions were soft, but lumpy. A glass coffee table sat in front of the couch. Two coasters and an empty Styrofoam burger container sat on it.

I sat.

Waiting.

Waiting on something. Nothing. Anything.

Something had to give. That's all I knew.

My head throbbed. My soul ached.

Confusion was my norm. I tried and tried to figure out why.

Especially now. I had everything I could want. What was wrong with me? Why couldn't I be happy? Even a little bit happy.

A shiny ribbon of red trickled down my arm. I let it run to the elbow and watched the dark drip form at the curve and then fall to the carpet.

The sight of my own blood gave me an initial lift. But, it only lasted a minute or two. The doom was in me. I couldn't shake it. I'd had a few beers, smoked a joint that a buddy had given me the day before, and gone for a walk down to the old grey barn. I'd even tried fishing in the pond next to my house. Nothing.

A few beers usually did the trick. But not this time. It took eight just to get a good buzz.

A tight fist began to squeeze my insides…down in my guts. A familiar gnawing kind of cramp. I knew what it meant. I knew where I had to go. I hated driving over there, but I needed it. I opened the banged-up tail gate of my truck and Z-Bo jumped right in. He never cared where we were going, he just wanted to go. Since moving out to the trailer, he'd become my closest friend.

We spent almost every spare minute together. He always trotted close behind when I was on the tractor shredding the pasture or cutting hay. Fishing in the tank usually ended with him jumping in and muddying up the water. He had a special spot at the end of my bed, but he usually ended up under the covers with me.

The truck swerved side to side when we sped out onto the gravel road. I didn't slow for the turn and almost ended up in the opposite ditch. I instinctively looked back to make sure Z-Bo was still there. I knew he would be. He never fell out. He loved to ride.

Evening shadows were becoming permanent as I passed the Smithville City Limit sign. I made the second right before the railroad tracks and eased along the dimly lit little street. I slowed and killed the engine as I rounded the last corner and rolled to a stop in the gravel parking lot of the projects.

The orange glow from the shitty little bulb directed me toward the right apartment. The air was thick, and my lip beaded with sweat as I stood in front of the beat up red door. It was cracked and faded. A few scattered pieces of paint had fallen off and added some color to the well-worn welcome mat below.

He wasn't my regular dealer, but I was betting he had enough crank to get me through the weekend. I owed my regular guy some money anyway.

The projects scared me. I'd been a banker for a few months now and kept thinking that I would somehow change. Something inside me would shift and I'd feel like a good person. Responsible. Upstanding.

I shouldn't be in the projects.

I shouldn't be buying crank from this fucking guy.

I shouldn't even know this fucking guy.

Friends from high school lived there, but that didn't make it any less scary. I'd heard stories of people being shot and stabbed and beat up in this very apartment complex.

I stood there for a minute or two. My hand reached out on its own and knocked. Once. Twice. Three times.

Fuck.

Distant beeping. Constant. Louder, and then quiet again. What the hell was it? I slogged through the fog of sleep and started to gain consciousness. Beeping. Louder than before, but still distant. Whining. Beeping. Whining. Something cold nudged me, and I opened my eyes. Table legs. Carpet. Beer cans on their sides. Puke. Two wadded up five-dollar bills. Z-Bo nudged me again. He needed to go outside and pee. And I needed to turn off the fucking alarm clock.

The beeping clock indicated that it was noon.

Monday. Fuck.

My alarm only went off on weekdays.

I was supposed to have been at work at 8 am. We always got there an hour before opening to get our trays of money sorted before the rush. I picked up the yellow receiver, extended the antenna, and dialed.

"Not going to make it." My head pounded as I mumbled the words.

Z-Bo shot through the door as I cracked it open to let him out. He peed on his regular trees and all four of my truck tires. He made his rounds and came back in as I listened to the bank manager's voice.

She wasn't happy. This wasn't the first time.

"I'm sick."

I wasn't lying. I couldn't remember anything.

As I hung up, thoughts swirled through my mind and out into the stale room as my spirits spiraled and seemed to fall onto the matted carpet. My body felt like rubber. Heavy. Wet. Gooey.

I'm not cut out for this shit. Any of it.

I'm not a banker.

I can't even go to work.

I searched in vain for something else. There had to be something. I tried to focus on good times. Family. Parties. Lynn. I couldn't stand the thought of her without me. The thought of me without her. She'd become a flickering memory. On again. Off again. Now, mostly off. It was an ending point. A jumping off place.

My eyes searched the room. Was this all there was? Was this it? A dirty, cluttered little trailer? Dishes piled high, stinking? Laundry on the floor? Sticker burs in the worn carpet? Ants trailing in and out of the dog food?

I laid back down and closed my eyes, stretching out on my back. My hands folded on my chest. Legs straight. Back to a peaceful place. The only peaceful place. A recurring vision of my death. My insides started to warm and the swirl of jagged thoughts slowed.

I was in my coffin again. My long hair flowed across my shoulders. The crisp white button down was open at the top, revealing the tiniest glint from a thick gold chain. Lynn had given me that chain. She was there.

Everyone was there. The walls were covered in pictures. My first deer. That great fishing trip. My senior photo. Me and Lynn. Me and my family. I looked happy in the photos.

Was I really happy?

I couldn't remember. I didn't think so.

They all stood around staring down at me. I didn't look stiff or pale. Just asleep. Waiting for someone to wake me and tell me everything would be okay.

Mom and Dad were crying. Wondering aloud if they could have done something different.

My buddies were laughing. Passing around a small flask and talking about some of the dumb shit we'd done.

"I hope he knew how much I loved him." Lynn stood with Blake and his girlfriend. She just kept repeating it.

I was silent.

I was happy.

The right corner of my mouth was slightly upturned – not really a smile, more like a smirk. No brain storm. No thought tornado. Peace. It was a peace I hadn't felt in a long, long time. It was a peace I only felt when I was there.

Z-Bo's pink wet tongue snapped me back to present.

Fuck.

I'm here.

No peace here.

I just had to figure out how to get there. Really there. And stay there.

But It had to look like an accident. I couldn't pin the stigma of suicide on my family. I wouldn't.

FORTY-SEVEN

It was a thick stack. The green bills looked ironed…only a few had curled edges. They were all fives. Red paper straps held each bundle of a hundred bills together, and they were rubber-banded in twos. I hesitated, and then moved my bag closer to the small safe and slid two money bricks in.

What the fuck am I doing?

I was alone in the drive-through building. No one was there, and there wasn't a camera in that location.

Fear grabbed me. I could still put it back. No one had seen me drop it in the bag.

No. It'll be easy.

I'm going to replace it.

I only needed the money for one week. I'd pay the dealer today, get the dope, sell the dope, and put the money back the following Monday before anyone missed it. It seemed easy.

The plan blew up on Friday. With my limited knowledge of how the drive-through worked, I'd neglected to account for the end of the week tally. When all the money was taken back to the main bank building, the receipts were reconciled with the cash from the small drive-through safe. The two-thousand dollars wasn't there.

Numbness took me over—a tingly distant numbness that I usually felt when put on the spot. A meeting was called. Everyone was there. Money was missing. It had to be found. I tried not to look as if I was trying not to look suspicious.

Everyone who'd had contact with the bills was questioned. We sat in a circle staring at everything but each other. I kept my eyes on the long grey filing cabinets along the back wall.

"How could it have disappeared?" the bank manager asked. I watched through the corner of my eye as she paced back and forth in the small space and waved her hands around.

"It must have gotten lost during delivery to the drive-through," a teller said. She placed her hand on the shoulder of the person next to her.

"Maybe they threw it in the trash with the delivery box," someone else chimed in as she stared daggers at the two ladies who usually worked the drive through.

Everyone had an opinion on what had happened.

I did not.

The search began. I looked under tables and assisted with the dumpster, adjacent to the drive-through building. Vanished. It was gone.

I wouldn't be replacing the money. I'd snorted too much of it up my nose. Almost three times the amount of crank I'd allotted for myself. Even if I could sell the rest, I'd be five or six hundred dollars short. It was no use. I'd just have to go along with the ruse and hope no one figured it out. Figured me out.

Guilt.

The collateral damage from my theft had left the workers who usually managed the drive through in a state of suspicion, embarrassment, and disarray. They had taken the brunt of the blame for the money loss. No one suspected that they stole it. Everyone thought they'd probably lost it. New rules were adopted, and old, long standing traditions were done away with. The drive-through team was officially broken up and every teller in the bank now had to do drive through rotations. The drive-through team was placed in that rotation and had to regularly work in the main lobby. They had been a duo over there for years. Everyone in town knew that they were the drive-through girls. They were crushed. I was a piece of shit. Darkness really settled in after that week. I couldn't pull myself from under that blanket. Taking the money had created a new low for me. Not just thoughts and feelings. I was a fucking thief.

Guilt. Shame. Sadness. They were eating me from the inside. I began to make some concrete plans for my suicide.

Confiding in the bank president and a few friends and family members, I planted the suspicion that someone was following me. I played it up a bit, and even started carrying a gun. Neal loaned me a big green repossessed Suburban, so that whoever was following me wouldn't immediately know it was me.

"You can do some undercover scouting and recon," he'd said as we drove around looking at cattle. "And hopefully catch someone acting suspicious."

We frequently rode around and checked on his cows and other bank assets. We drank a lot of beer. And try as I may to keep a wall up between us because of the guilt I felt for taking the money, I just couldn't. He had an easy way about him and he made me feel comfortable for those brief bits of time.

I needed to tell him. I desperately wanted to tell him everything. But the words never came.

A few days rolled by and things at the bank calmed. No one talked about the money. But, no one seemed themselves either.

Sideways glances. Short, snappy conversations. All business.

I was back up front, cashing checks and taking deposits. My upper lip glistened as I looked down at the drawer full of bills – ones, fives, tens, twenties. I tried to ignore the guilt. It surrounded me like a bubble.

The phone rang. It wasn't the old fashion ring, but more of a digital, bank lobby kind of ring.

Fuck.

I'd been waiting for it to ring for over an hour. Surely someone needed to call the bank.

I picked it up and stretched the twisted cord to its maximum length.

"Yes," I said. "Okay."

I placed the receiver back on the hook and started for the door. The manager looked concerned as I walked by her desk.

"Emergency out at the place," I lied.

I left quickly before she could start asking questions.

A great sadness came over me as I drove the twenty minutes from the bank to the ranch. I'd gone over this a hundred times in my head. I'd even left the bank twice before, thinking that those would be the days. They weren't, but this day was.

The day that I would end my life.

A weight kind of lifted, and for a brief moment on that narrow winding road, I saw things more clearly than ever before. There were trees and ponds I'd never seen. A red-tailed hawk made his tight circles just above the tree-line. A newborn calf followed its mother back to the herd for its big introduction. Houses and barns and buildings appeared out of nowhere. How could I have missed all that?

FORTY-EIGHT

I drove through the cattle guard and up the grass-lined dirt road. My skinny trailer sat there as if waiting. I jumped out of the suburban and ran in quickly. The small box of green-tipped matches were on the table, right where I'd left them that morning. The gas can was sitting in the sun and had swollen and bulged out a bit. I put the can in the back of the truck. The matches rattled in my pocket as I jumped in.

As I started toward the barn I noticed Z-Bo streaking down the path behind me. He didn't know where I was going, but he wanted to come, too.

I stopped the truck. My heart stopped with it.

What the fuck?

I couldn't leave him behind.

He's too big for anybody to handle.

He's a pit bull.

He'll be so confused without me.

My mind churned for a few seconds and the thought popped into my head. I didn't think I could do it.

I got out and banged the tail-gate down. He jumped in and we turned around and headed back up to the house.

The sand was soft as I stepped down and dropped the tail-gate again. He followed me into the shade of the Black-Jack Oak on the side of the house.

Tears burst from my eyes. I crumbled to the ground beside him.

"You deserve better than me, buddy."

I hugged him.

"But I can't leave you here."

I tossed the rope over the lowest limb of the oak. He looked excited, probably thinking we were about to have our usual tug-of-war. Bark dust floated down through the soft light. One more long hug.

I can't do it.

The limb didn't budge as I pulled down on the end of the rope and turned my head away. I felt him struggle for a minute, maybe two.

When all movement had stopped, I let go of the rope and slogged toward the truck.

It was done.

He was done.

I was done.

I sobbed as I opened the squeaky truck door. I had to get on with it…now.

No second thought. No second look. I jumped in and made my way back down the hill.

The shadowed half-open door of the old wooden barn beckoned. The smell of freshly cut hay filled my nostrils as I walked in. I quickly created a small stack of older dry yellowish hay in the corner, just inside the door. I eased down to my knees and stopped for a second. One last look around.

This is it.

Mom. Dad. Brothers. Sister. Lynn. Friends. Cousins. Pets. Everything and everyone I'd ever known. My mind filled with images. I was about to leave it all behind. Dusty hay crumbs swirled in the soft breeze and stuck to the streams of tears on my cheeks.

I struck the match and moved it toward the little stack in front of me. Orange flames engulfed the pile. The hot jumping fire leaped from my stack and engulfed the first dry bail it found. It exploded. Then a second. Then a third. Smoke quickly filled the whole barn.

Breathe in.

I'd gone over it in my mind a hundred times.

Breathe in.

Come on. Again.

Was I breathing smoke…or fire? I couldn't tell.

Breathe in.

I coughed. Wretched. Heaved.

Thick white smoke. That was all.

Fear and excitement were waging a small war in my mind. I was afraid to die. I was excited to die. I was dying.

Thunder. Rumbling thunder. My eyes cracked open and I immediately squeezed them shut. Burning. Coughing. Again. And, again. I threw up and then coughed some more. The stinging was unbearable. My throat. My lungs. My eyes. My face.

What the fuck?

I opened my eyes again and regretted it. They had to be on fire. They stung. Like fire ants. I opened them.

I could see the inferno through the tall weeds. Orange and yellow curls coming out of the doorway. Liquid yellow flames peeking and running through each cracked grey slat. It was burning without me.

What the fuck?

I was supposed to be in there. I was supposed to be dead.

Panic began to rise up in my burning throat. Tears flowed and I couldn't seem to think straight.

Somehow, I'd made it out of the barn and ran a hundred yards or so up the hill before collapsing. Instinct, or angels had taken over. Some force had dragged my pathetic body out of the smoke and flames and lain me to rest in a soft bed of coastal Bermuda grass and dove weed.

I rounded the side corner of the little trailer house and froze.

Oh no.

Oh fucking no.

He was still. Completely still. Laying on the ground in the sand and shade. Under the oak.

I'd taken his life and not my own.

He was dead. I was alive.

My eyes quickly found the ground as I turned and went around the other way. I jog-walked to the back porch and up the weathered wooden steps. I looked back, searching the sky, hoping for rainclouds.

Maybe some of the barn will be okay. I knew it wouldn't.

Soft white cotton balls, high in the sky, whiffed by as the soft southerly breeze carried them north. The tower of grey and white smoke from the barn lifted and bent toward town. My lungs burned.

The phone.

Call the fire department.

The cold water stung my throat as I downed the glass. Then another. I splashed some on my face and wiped it off with a dirty hand-towel.

"9-1-1, can I help you?"

"My barn is on fire."

I was watching it burn through my kitchen window.

I hung up and ran back down the hill. The inferno still raged. The entire barn was engulfed in blinding colors. The tower of smoke rose up as far as my eyes could see. There was no top. No end. Just flame and smoke.

I heard the sirens, even though I'd only hung up a few seconds ago. Someone else must have called. A wall of heat stopped me fifty yards or so from the barn. I couldn't get closer.

What am I going to do?

They were coming.

My guts came alive. I thought I might have diarrhea. My stomach heaved, but nothing came up. A hawk was trapped in my chest and trying to get out. I felt her wings pounding as she bounced from side to side, rib to rib.

Small fires had begun to spring up in the open field in front of the barn. I cracked the stem of a green sage bush and started whacking at the nearest hot spot. Ash, soot, and tiny flaming pieces of grass flew up and into my face. A convoy of volunteer fire fighters and neighbors rolled through the gate on the north end of the property and quickly surrounded the barn. A frantic mob scrambled around the field swatting at the smaller fires, while a firetruck pulled as close to the barn as possible and let loose the water. The stiff white stream left the hose with good intention, but upon nearing the inferno, it dissipated into a translucent cloud of steam. It had no impact on the heat or the blaze.

"It's too late," a wiry, soot-covered volunteer said. "We'll just have to let it burn out."

As the final hot spots were being put down, I reached for the loose thoughts flying around in my head. A story. I had to put together a story. I hadn't prepared for this. I wasn't supposed to be here. I was supposed to be dead. They were supposed to put the pieces together and make up their own story. With the adrenaline slowly leaving my bloodstream, I became aware of my burning eyes and my lungs felt as if I'd inhaled burning straws of hay, and not smoke. My eyes watered and I could barely see who all was standing around. The crowd was congratulating each other on a job well done. Trucks and cars were haphazardly parked along the entrance road. A beat-up pickup had tried to make it around the north end of the field and sank in the soft sand. Another truck was pulling it out with a long rusty chain. Two blurry men were jumping in the bed of the stuck truck, trying to add some traction to the rear wheels.

I took short slow strides up the hill toward my house. Neal was streaking up the hill in his truck. He came to a stop in a cloud of dust and quickly jumped out.

"Someone killed my dog."

"What?" his face went white.

"He's over by the side of the house."

I couldn't make myself look in that direction.

"Someone called me at the bank," I lied again. "They told me to get home right away."

I'd left work quickly, so it all sounded legitimate.

"When I drove up, the barn was smoking, and my dog was swinging from the tree." I genuinely sobbed.

"Oh damn," he said.

"It must have happened right before I got here, because the fire was still pretty small, and my Z-Bo was still warm."

"Shit." He put his hand on my shoulder.

"I tried to put out the fire, but it was no use," I said.

That was it. I didn't feel the need to say more, and he didn't ask.

We took turns scooping the reddish sand from the hole. Neither of us said a word. I stepped out of the shallow grave, looked it over, and walked toward my dog a few feet away.

What the fuck? How could I have done this?

My mind was racing again. Everything was blurry. My heart pounded as if the hawk might bust out of me at any moment. Neal followed me over and helped me place Z-Bo in his final resting place. I cried and watched him disappear beneath the sand. One scoop at a time.

I wanted to tell Neal. It was about to explode from my chest. My secrets clawed their way up. Up from the pit of my stomach. Through my heart.

They stuck in my throat again.

I didn't want to lie anymore. I wanted to tell someone. His hand was warm and strong on my shoulder once more.

"We'll do whatever it takes to find them," he vowed. "We'll make them pay."

We locked eyes for a second, and I looked away.

"Thanks," I whispered.

But wait.

There's something…

No. I couldn't tell him. I imagined the disappointment he'd feel. I couldn't let him down. I couldn't let Mom and Dad down. I couldn't let all my friends down. They all expected me to be great. I had to be great. But I knew I wasn't.

FORTY-NINE

I always held out hope. I always thought we'd get back together. Even though I'd been drunk so many times and fucked so many people that I couldn't remember them all, I always knew it would be us.

Maybe this time.

Lynn had been going to school about two hours from town but came home every other weekend or so. Sometimes she called. Sometimes she didn't.

This weekend she'd called. We'd ridden around town for a while and came back to her parent's house on the hill. We'd just finished doing what we always did when we had the house to ourselves. She seemed distracted.

She pretended to re-arrange some plants on the tiny back porch. As much as I wanted to hear her voice, I wasn't sure I wanted to hear what she had to say. Something was off. An unusual nervous energy seemed suspended in the air between us.

"I love you," I said.

"I'm kind of dating someone at school." She twirled the tip of her shiny brown hair as she said the words.

It was a gut punch. I thought I might throw up right there in the yard. I wanted to scream. The yell formed in my mouth.

"What?" I asked softly.

"It's not that serious," she assured me. "We've only gone out a couple times."

"Okay. Guess I'll just go get fucked up."

"I know you will," she said. Sadness and worry lined her brow.

We talked some more about the crazy shit that had happened the previous weekend. I repeated the story of the fire, my dog, the insanity of it all. My guts turned inside out as I lied.

There was something wrong with me. Deep down. Something wrong.

She didn't know it. She just loved me. She couldn't know it. No one could. I'd hid it so well. It had been my secret. Every memory of every moment of my life was clouded by what I'd become inside. What I always felt I was at some level. I'd been working my ass off to prove to myself that it was true. I was bad. Somehow inherently bad. I was broken. He had broken me.

I couldn't undo it. No matter how hard I tried, I stayed broken. Nothing I did helped. I was done.

She loved me. She couldn't fix me.

"I'm going to go," I said.

"You don't have to."

"But I do," I whispered. "I won't share you."

She was saying something as I rounded the house and walked toward the front yard. I couldn't understand her. I didn't care.

I sat in my truck for a full minute. The door was still open. My left foot dangled as if waiting for me to tell it whether to get in or get out.

I can get her back.

I knew I couldn't. I struggled to find my breath.

I'm not going to cry.

I didn't.

The door closed softly as I pulled forward.

I drove around the corner and stopped. Shuffling through my cassettes, I found the one I wanted. When the bass intro hit, I made a quick U-turn and headed back to town.

One last glance at her house as I sped by. I cranked up Loverboy's "Turn Me Loose" as loud as it would go and punched the gas to the floor.

Fuck. I guess that's that.

Sad. But angry, also. Angry at myself.

The old movies kept replaying in my head. Soft nights snuggling on the couch. Pizza and movies. And...all those times I'd fucked her over. All the lies. The lies about the lies. It should have been so easy to love her.

If I'd been better, maybe she would have stuck with me.

But I'm not.

I'm not better.

I'm a no-good piece of...

Right turn.

It came out of nowhere and caught me off guard. The rear tires let out a deep howl as the truck skidded to a stop.

My fists clenched at the thought of her holding someone else's hand.

I need a fucking beer.

Luckily, there were a few left in the cooler. I hoped they were still cold.

I gripped the steering wheel and slammed the pedal to the floor again. The rear of the truck skidded around to the left as I made the right turn.

The Burger Joint was just up the road. Chili-cheese bacon cheese burger. My favorite.

I wasn't really hungry but pulled in anyway. I could sit there and stare out the large front window. If any of my friends were out and about, they'd pull in when they saw my truck.

The glass door banged behind me and her head appeared from behind the ice-cream machine. I knew her, but not really.

"What can I get you?" she said

"Um...when did you start working here?"

"About a week ago," her voice was bubbly.

"Cool," I grinned. "What time do you get off?" I was half joking.

"In about an hour."

"I'll eat and wait." I said with confidence. "Chili-cheese bacon cheeseburger and tater tots with cheese."

"Okay."

"Okay what?"

"Okay to both," she looked me right in the eyes when she spoke. "Both."

She smiled when she came over to check on me. The tater tots she'd brought over a while before weren't visible under the Ketchup.

"Do you need some food with all that ketchup?" she giggled.

"Nope. I'm good,"

"I get off in ten," she whispered.

"I'll be outside."

Five minutes later, she bounced out of the building and jumped in the passenger side of my truck.

"Where to?"

"Doesn't matter," she flashed a devilish grin.

Neal's house was close, and it would be empty. He only stayed on the weekdays so that he didn't have to drive in to work from Austin. Without a word, I backed out of the parking spot and pulled away. The bright sign was already on for the evening. Someone had broken the glass. The J in Joint was dark.

The strong smell of Chlorine assaulted my nose. The pool house was tiny, and the hot tub room had been closed up since Neal left for the city.

She slid the shirt over her head and removed the bra, in one graceful movement. I was still staring at her boobs when her pants hit the floor. I was fumbling with the buttons on my Levis when she knocked my hand away and eased down onto her knees.

Holy Shit.

I glanced back at the main house again just to make sure he wasn't home. The small pool house was a hundred yards or so from the main house, and I didn't want anyone surprising us.

She had me ready. Her abs flexed as she laid back on the green artificial grass carpet.

She was ready too. She pulled me down on top of her and we started moving immediately. She was desperate. So was I.

I needed it. Fast. Hard.

"Tell me you love me," I moaned.

"I love you." She said between heavy breaths.

I knew she didn't. I didn't care.

"Tell me again," I said.

"I love you. I love you. Don't stop."

If Lynn wouldn't love me, somebody would.

"Don't stop," she said again. "Don't ever stop."

We used each other for a solid hour. The rough texture of the turf carpet had burned a raspberry on both of my knees.

'Finish with me," she begged.

We locked eyes as we jerked and shook. She cried out one last time and went limp. I rested my forehead on her shoulder and we both struggled in the thick air to catch our breath. Neither of us moved.

The love I'd needed a second before wafted up and disappeared into the dingy light with the swirling steam from the hot tub.

FIFTY

Mugginess. My shirt stuck to my back. Condensation ran down the silver
sides of the can and dripped from the fat part of my hand and onto my
dirty carpet. I carefully stacked the empty on top of the other eleven. I
didn't feel drunk, but I didn't dare drink anymore, for fear of fucking up
what I hoped would be my last attempt at ending my life. I looked around
the small space. Everything was in its place. I'd finally washed and put away
the sink full of dirty dishes.

No one was expecting me.

It was time.

I eased the door open and walked down the steps. One foot rested
softly on the sand, and then the other. The matches rattled in my pocket. I
made the corner of the house and got down on my knees. The pink and
yellow insulation disintegrated as I tore the plastic cover off and moved it
out of the way. Small glittery itchy crystals found their way onto my sweaty
arm.

I scratched the box and waited until the small purple flame jumped
from the tip of the match. It barely caught the dry cracked paper lining
between the insulation and the floor of my little home. The smoke seemed
to disappear into the cotton candy layer. It caught fast. I had to hurry.

I'd obsessively thought it through. A big enough flame to catch
the rest, but small enough for me to make it back inside the trailer, lock the
door, get into bed and pull the covers over my head for the last time. Easy.
Lay there. Wait. Breathe in a few times.

Thunder pounded in my head as I anticipated the smoke.

What if the flames come first?
What if I'm not unconscious when the flames come?
What if I burn...awake and alive?
My mind tumbled.
Stay. Run. Stay. Run.
The smoke still hadn't penetrated the shell of the trailer. I couldn't see it. I couldn't smell it.
What the fuck? This should be easy.
I fumbled with the back door and jumped off the wobbly porch. The water hose was wound around the short white pipe like a green snake. I spun the valve on the faucet and ran over to where I'd lit what I thought would be a fire. Nothing. Only smoke and some glowing remnants of the paper that was wrapped around the insulation. It twinkled like a bed of pink jewels in the dark. A gentle breeze caused them to pop and crack and sizzle. The insulation smoldered like the end of a cigar but hadn't produced any flames after the paper layer mostly burned off.

Steam erupted when the water contacted the bright embers. I sprayed and sprayed until I didn't see anymore.
Now what? How do I explain this?
Shame and panic set in as I realized I'd failed again. Just like waking up in the weeds after the barn fire, I now had to create a story. Something that would seem believable. I carefully rolled the hose back up.
I knew what I had to do.

Gravel shot out from behind the truck as the all-terrain tires tried with little success to find traction on the loose road. I was outrunning the headlight beam on the curvy, winding road. I rounded the last corner, swerved right, and jumped the cattle guard into my closest neighbor's driveway. She looked terrified as she came to the door. I yelled the words.
"Call the fire department. Someone set my trailer on fire. "
I jumped in the truck and sped back in the direction I'd come. The truck rocked up and down as I flew around each corner and over each bump of the narrow little county road.

Now what? Total darkness from under the house. Yellow broken light danced on the tree limbs above the house. Moths and their kin flew in circles around the orangey glow of the porch light.
So, I'd tried to burn myself again...and fucked it up.

Guilt, shame, and an overwhelming sense of failure swept over me. So I just sat there…waiting.

The whirring of the sirens reached my ears first. Faint. Gone. No, there it was. The fire department was on the way. I had no idea what I'd say. I didn't really care. The soft breeze brought the smell of burnt insulation and plastic to my nostrils. I watched as the two trucks raced up the gravel driveway.

They rounded the last corner by the big fence post and made their way to the house. I straightened my legs and hopped off the tailgate.

"Where's the fire?" three guys jumped out of the first truck in unison.

"Under the house…over on that end," I answered.

They tore at the bottom of the trailer like bears rooting up old stumps. Charred pieces of paper caught the wind and blew in circles until they disappeared into the darkness.

"What happened," the firefighter asked.

"Something woke me up and I smelled smoke," I answered.

"Did you see anything? Hear anything?"

"Nope, nothing. I was asleep."

That's all I could come up with. Numbness made its way from my brain, down into my core, and out into my limbs. I didn't want to talk. I didn't feel like piecing together a story for these guys. I didn't want to lie.

"Why is the water hose rolled up neatly like that?" the Chief asked.

"I sprayed the trailer until I thought the fire was out and then wrapped it back up." That was it. The truth.

I went back in the house and called Mom.

"Can I stay at your house tonight?"

"Yes. What's wrong?"

"There was a fire."

"What?" She sounded frantic.

"I'll tell you about it when I get there."

I hung up and followed the fire trucks to town.

Mom was waiting in the front yard when I pulled in. Her face was twisted. She looked terrified. It was the second time in a month someone had set fire at my place. This time they'd tried to hurt me.

It had been hard to lie to her and Dad about the barn fire. They'd scrambled around and made me repeat the story over and over. Hoping. Praying. There had to be an answer.

"Why would someone want to hurt you?"

Lies.

The old rusted chains creaked as I slumped down on the front porch swing. It rocked back and forth on its own. I stared straight ahead.

"Did you see anything?" Dad asked.

"Nope."

"Who the hell would do this?"

"I wish I knew."

"Damn. The dog, the barn, and now this."

"I know."

"Maybe you should just move back to town."

"I might."

As Dad asked more questions I'd already answered, I just nodded. I had nothing left. My insides were empty. I was already dead. I just couldn't seem to end it.

FIFTY-ONE

Three weeks crawled by. Hard weeks. Mostly drunk and cranked out.

I was staying at Mom and Dad's. I'd gone back out to the trailer and grabbed a few things.

Seeing Z-Bo's spot on the couch was too much. I'd sat on the floor and sobbed, and just left the other stuff I'd planned on taking.

"It still smells like smoke," I'd said when I got back to town. "I can't sleep there."

"That's okay honey," Mom had said. "Stay here as long as you need to."

I'd wrecked my truck again and now she was having to take me to work.

As she eased down the road searching for a different radio station, I stared at the floor mat below my feet.

The words were there. They weren't words I wanted to speak. I hadn't planned on telling her. I knew I was about to. I knew she could hear my heart beating. The space inside the car was shrinking. We were running out of air. I couldn't breathe.

I can't do it.

Jump out.

My fingers gripped the metal door handle. I eased it upward.

"Can you stop the car?" I whispered.

"What?"

"Please stop the car."

She did. We were just down the street from her house. Live Oak limbs stretched across the road above us.

"I did it, Mom."

"Did what?"

"All of it. It was me. No one is after me."

Silence.

I breathed in. The hawk in my chest flapped and clawed, looking for a way out.

"The fires. My dog. Passing out. Me. All me. All lies."

Silence.

The words had erupted from my soul like hot lava. Tears streamed down my face. I watched from outside my body as I ripped my mom's heart out. She just stared out the window. Tears began to show in the corners of her eyes.

And finally I let loose the words I'd held on to for all those years...what he'd done to me. What I'd endured.

What she hadn't noticed.

What no one had warned me about.

What they hadn't stopped.

What no one had protected me from.

What I'd let happen.

Her face slowly whitened. Her jaw muscles rippled as she absorbed what I'd just told her. She turned to me with a shocked look on her face.

I was punching her in the gut with each new revelation. I was cutting her skin over and over with the sound of my voice. I was crushing her soul. There was nothing she could do about it. No way to go back and change it. No way to take it away.

I flinched as she moved. The leather seat squeaked as her trembling arms came toward me and wrapped me up.

She hugged me. Just hugged me.

The car was still running. The air conditioner had created condensation on my window.

Our tears ran together as we sobbed.

She slumped down in her seat and ran her thumb along the top of the steering wheel. We sat there on the side of the pot holey street. Neither of us knew what to do. Where to go. How to move past this.

"I need to get to the bank. I'm late for work."

She sat up and wiped the black trail of makeup from under her eyes. The car lurched forward when she put it in drive. Neither of us said anything else.

I watched her. Wondered what she was thinking. The doubts and regrets she must have been grappling with.

Does she think I blame her?

I couldn't bring myself to ask.

I didn't want to talk about it anymore. I'd said all I could in that moment. She didn't seem to want to talk anymore either. Maybe she was afraid there was more.

How could there be more?

"I love you," I said, just to make sure she knew.

"I love you too." Her voice cracked just a little. "It's all going to be okay now. It's all going to be okay."

As we drove toward the bank, the hawk slowed its beating wings. The swirling thoughts in my head began to eddy.

The emotion of our conversation slowly dissolved, like salt in warm water. Something had shifted…ever so slightly. Something inside me.

The sun broke free of the clouds and warmed my skin. The smell of Live Oak leaves and freshly mown grass wafted through the half open window.

I leaned back against the head-rest and closed my eyes.

I saw myself standing next to our loud little ice cream maker on the front porch so many years ago. Little me. Plaid homemade pants. Cowlick sticking up on the crown of my head. Smiling. Waiting for that taste…that vanilla…the only thing that mattered.

It's all going to be okay now.

It's all going to be okay.

FIFTY-TWO

"Do you think you have a problem?"

"I guess."

"This is the third time you've been in jail this month."

Only a couple of feet separated us in the small space.

"Unlucky, I guess."

"You think it's really just your luck?"

"Maybe. Maybe not."

"If you keep going like this, you'll be dead in a year."

"Fuck, probably. I wouldn't mind that so much."

"Do you really want to die? I mean really?"

I waited for his answer. When he didn't give it, I took my feet off the desk and looked directly into his eyes.

"I've been there man," I said.

I glanced at the walls of my small office. I'd accumulated quite a collection in that short year. Posters. Magazine cut-outs. Pictures of pine trees and sunsets. And near the door...the Problem Bag. I'd noticed him staring at it as he avoided my eyes.

"Just write down anything that's bothering you," I said, "And put it in the bag. I burn that shit once a week. With the flames and smoke, go the problems."

"You've really done the same shit I have?" he asked.

"Yep," I answered. "And some you haven't."

He sat up a bit. Seeming to start listening for the first time.

"So, what happened?" he leaned closer to my desk. "How'd you stop?"

"I sat where you're sitting," I said. "And did what you're doing."

"Really?"

"Yep. I was sick and tired of being sick and tired."

I shuffled through his paperwork. He'd been honest. He'd held no punches.

Goosebumps rose on my forearms when I thought back to that day. My first day. Those questions. My answers. His answers.

"And, you're really happy?" he asked. "Really?"

I assured him that I was.

AFTERWORD

This is my story. My path. I'll never know why these things happened. Truthfully, it doesn't matter to me anymore. I'm proud to be able to discuss it with you.

There are thousands of men out there who've had similar experiences and had their lives wrecked. It's hard to talk about. It's hard to listen to. It's uncomfortable and scary. If we could only tell. Get it out in the open. Put the light of day on it.

I'm so excited to still be walking this path and to start this new chapter as a spokesperson for all those boys and men out there who can't imagine ever opening up about this.

I'm here.

I truly believe we need to share our stories and support one another in any way we can. If you've had this happen to you...tell someone. If you don't have anyone to tell...tell me. Feel free to contact me at the website below if you just need to get it off your chest. I won't reply unless you ask me to. Just the act of hitting "send" and relieving yourself of the burden could make a difference. And if you're not ready for that yet, I hope this book has helped you realize that you're not alone. We're in this together. It's going to be okay.

My life is filled with abundance, success, and joy today. If I can get here, so can you!

If you'd like to be a part of the conversation, find me online at www.BradWatson.com and discover what you can do to help. I would love to speak to you, your group, or at your event.

Made in the USA
Middletown, DE
11 May 2021